Minutes of the Lower Forty

MINUTES
of the
LOWER FORTY

by Corey Ford

Illustrated by Walter Dower

HOLT, RINEHART AND WINSTON
New York

Published simultaneously in Canada by Holt,
Rinehart and Winston of Canada, Limited.

First Edition

Library of Congress Catalog Card Number: 62–9209

"The Lower Forty" appears as a regular monthly feature in
Field & Stream, where the stories in this collection had their first
publication. The author wishes to thank the publisher for permission to reprint these selections.

Some of the stories appeared originally under other titles: "Puppy
Love" as "A Friend for Timmie," "The Prize Sucker" as "The
World-Record Sucker," "A Lesson in Taxidair-r-my" as "A Lesson
in Taxidermy," "No Hunting or Trespassing" as "The Horns of
Temptation," and "How to Carve a Turkey" as "The Do-It-
Yourself Turkey." "Seat of Justice" appeared as "The Judge Holds
Court" and "Strictly for the Birds" appeared as "Love the Little
Birdies" in an earlier collection, *You Can Always Tell a Fisherman.*

Designer: Ernst Reichl

82888–0412
Printed in the United States of America

FOR

Hugh and Caroline Grey

Foreword

Here are the minutes of the Lower Forty Shooting, Angling and Inside Straight club, as recorded by the secretary during the club's occasional meetings in Uncle Perk's store. You know Uncle Perk's store ("Jno. Perkins, Prop., Guns & Fshng Tckle, Bot Sold & Swopt"). The smell of ground coffee and harness leather and kerosene. A potbellied stove, a wedge of rattrap cheese on the counter, a glass showcase with peppermint candy that must be every bit of two years old. Nobody can remember when the display window in front of the store was last washed. Several years ago somebody caught Uncle Perk wiping a patch bare in the center of the pane. "Cleaning your window so people can see in?" he asked. "Naw," Uncle Perk replied, "so I can see out."

Generally Uncle Perk sits in a swivel chair before his roll-top desk, his rubber hunting boots crossed on the blotter, smoking a rank corncob pipe and glowering at anyone who enters. He makes no move to rise when the string of sleigh bells inside the front door jangles. If a customer asks for something, he jerks a thumb toward the shelves. "You know where it is," he growls. "Go git it."

Customers are only a nuisance, but when the members of the Lower Forty gather in his store, well, that's something else again. Then Uncle Perk pulls down the shades, hangs a "Closed for Inventory" sign on the door, opens the lower left-hand drawer of his desk and takes out a jug of his special home-made Old Stump Blower. He passes it around to his fellow members, and the meeting comes to order—if any session of the Lower Forty could be called order.

They've been gathering in Uncle Perk's store for years, the same group of sportsmen you'd find in any small town anywhere. There's Judge Parker; and Doc Hall; and Colonel Cobb, who runs the Hardscrabble *Gazette;* and Cousin Sid, principal of the high school; and Dexter Smeed, the Judge's wife's nephew; and, of course, the local undertaker, Angus MacNab, whose hearse is used by the members on their overnight camping trips in exchange for a slight r-r-remuneration to r-r-reimburse Mr. MacNab for the wear and tear on his tir-r-res.

It's a very informal club, with no by-laws or regulations. Once Uncle Perk put a sheet of wrapping paper in his battered typewriter and tried to hammer out a constitution. He didn't get very far. All he wrote was:

Constituation of the Lower Fourty

<u>Artickle One</u>: Rules.
>> They ain't no rules.

<u>Artickle Two</u>: President.
>> Everybody's President.

<u>Artickle Three</u>: Membership.
>> If ennybody else wants to join this club,
>> go ahead, but don't bother us about it.
>> We've went fishing.

The constitution was filed away, and nobody can remember to this day where they put it, so the club still goes on as it always has. Judge Parker sounds forth pontifically, and Doc Hall needles him, and Mr. MacNab, the self-appointed treasurer, counts up the cash on hand for a game supper at Cousin Sid's camp, and Cousin Sid does the dishes afterward.

No, the Lower Forty will never change, because sportsmen never change. They're the same the world over, arguing and bragging and swapping tall tales around a jug and a dog and a fire. The Lower Forty is the name of this particular club, but it could be any club and any group of sportsmen who have hunted together in the cold, and fished in the rain, and shared the same memories over the years. . . .

So take this book of memories, and lean back in Uncle Perk's swivel chair, and cross your feet on his desk. Pull open the lower left-hand drawer, if you want, and help yourself to his jug of Old Stump Blower. You're a member of the Lower Forty too.

COREY FORD,
Secretary

Contents

xi

Minutes of the Lower Forty

Happy Birthday to Us

Cousin Sid stole another glance at his watch and gave his cabin a critical last-minute inspection. Festoons of red, white and blue crepe paper hung from the ceiling, the rack of antlers on the wall sprouted fresh balsam boughs, and a red ribbon graced the midriff of the stuffed trout over the fireplace. In the middle of the mantel stood the official emblem of the Lower Forty Shooting, Angling and Inside Straight Club—a rainbow rampant on a broken rod, with one fin on a Bible and the other upraised—and below it was lettered "Many Happy Returns!" The headlights of approaching cars shone in the window, and

Cousin Sid hastily struck a match and lit ten candles on a big chocolate cake reposing on the table.

Judge Parker halted in the doorway and stared at the candles blankly. "Wotinell is that?"

"It's a birthday cake," Cousin Sid beamed.

Doc Hall shouldered through the door behind the Judge, stamping snow from his boots onto Cousin Sid's rug. "Who's having a birthday?"

"We are," Cousin Sid reminded him, as the other members crowded in. "Don't you remember, fellows? This is the tenth anniversary of the founding of the Lower Forty, and I thought we ought to have some sort of celebration."

"Well, in that case," Judge Parker said promptly, clearing his throat, "such an auspicious occasion calls for a few appropriate remarks." He rested an elbow on the mantel and assumed his best judicial manner. "For ten long years," he began, "we have enjoyed the pleasure of each other's companionship in fair weather and foul, in sun and rain, in field and stream. We have shared each other's triumphs . . ."

"Like that two-pound squaretail I took right out from under your nose," Doc Hall goaded him.

The Judge scowled. ". . . and we have put up with each other's failures," he continued, with a dark look at Doc Hall, "such as that ten-point buck you missed standing stock-still at twenty yards . . ."

"Would ye conclude the or-r-ration, Judge," Mr. MacNab interrupted, "and blow out those candles? We could use them again next year."

Judge Parker expelled his breath in an indignant snort, extinguishing all ten candles at once, and unsheathed his hunting knife to cut the cake.

Cousin Sid held up his hand. "Wait a minute," he pleaded. "There's a little presentation we want to make first." He pointed to a package on the table, wrapped in tissue paper and ribbon. "For ten years the club has been holding its meetings in the back of Uncle Perk's store," he said, handing the package to Uncle Perk, "and some of us felt that it was high time we offered this slight token of our appreciation."

"Wal, naow, that's mighty nice of you fellas," Uncle Perk smiled, peeling off the tissue paper and revealing a brand-new jug of Old Stump Blower. "Why, it's my favorite brand, too," he exclaimed in surprise. "Where did you ever find it?"

"In the lower left-hand dr-r-rawer of your desk," Mr. MacNab conceded frankly.

"How about Cousin Sid?" Doc Hall inquired, moved by the sentimental spirit of the occasion. "We owe him a lot, too."

"Oh, we haven't forgotten our loyal Sidney," Colonel Cobb assured him, producing another gift. "Night after night the rest of us have sat around and relaxed after supper while Cousin Sid washed the dishes," he recalled. "So tonight we'd like to present him with this big economy-size box of Scrubbo soap flakes, to make his work easier."

Judge Parker gouged himself a large slab of birthday cake and sprawled in an easy chair beside the fire. "You know, it's hard to realize that ten years have gone by since this club started," he mused. "Those were the good old days. Yes sir, a lot of things have changed since then."

"It isn't like it used to be," Doc Hall agreed, licking chocolate from his fingers. "Take the fishing, for instance. It seems to me that trout are getting smaller lately," he sighed, "or else the creels are getting bigger."

"It's these modern scales," Uncle Perk grumbled. "They weigh everything lighter."

"They just don't put the same material into stuff any more," Colonel Cobb reflected, letting out his belt another notch. "The pants they sell you nowadays always seem to shrink, especially around the waist."

"The hunting isn't what it was, either," Judge Parker mourned. "Either the birds fly faster or the shotgun shells don't have as big a pattern as they used to."

"Streams are getting harder to wade, too," Doc Hall observed. "Rocks are more slippery and holes are deeper when you step into them."

"Fly lines aren't what they used to be," Mr. MacNab complained. "A mon can't get any distance any more."

"I've noticed the water is colder when you fall in," Cousin Sid added, "and it takes you longer to get dry when you get wet."

"Banks are steeper, too," Colonel Cobb nodded, "and the car isn't as near when you have to walk back to it."

"Strands of barbed wire are closer together when you crawl through them," Uncle Perk grunted.

"Hemlock trees are higher when you climb them to untangle your fly," said Doc Hall.

"Everything is farther away," Colonel Cobb maintained. "Like my hunting boots, when I stoop over to lace them up."

"It's the same with trout flies," Judge Parker frowned. "I

have to hold them at arm's length now to tie them on the leader. They don't make the eyes of the hooks as big these days."

"Another thing that's struck me lately," Colonel Cobb said. "They're putting more pockets in fishing jackets. I spend half an hour going through them trying to find my pipe, before I remember I left it at home."

"Pockets weigh more, too," Cousin Sid reflected, "because I have to take along more things when I go fishing, in case there's something I need that I don't have when I want it."

"Alarm clocks go off ear-r-rlier than they used to," Mr. Mac-Nab remarked.

"And the sun is hotter on my bald spot," admitted Colonel Cobb.

"And there's more mosquitoes," said Uncle Perk.

"And all the other fishermen you meet look so much older," Judge Parker chimed in. "Half the time I can't even place them any more. People named George turn out to be Bill, and they always call me Fred. Or maybe Harry."

"On the other hand," Doc Hall pointed out, "young people these days are much younger than they used to be when we were as young as they are."

There was a moody silence. Cousin Sid flipped the pages of the club album and displayed a pair of photographs. "Look at this picture of us taken ten years ago," he said, "and at this one taken the other day. Do you suppose by any chance we've changed ourselves?"

"Of course not," Judge Parker snorted. "They don't use the same kind of film in cameras any more, that's all."

"Personally I don't feel a day older," Doc Hall claimed.

"I'm the same as I always was," Colonel Cobb insisted, unbuttoning the top button of his trousers, "if not more so."

"Aye, we're all vair-r-ry well pr-r-resairved," Mr. MacNab agreed, with a significant glance at Uncle Perk's jug, "but there's nae harm in pr-r-resairving ourselves a wee bit more."

Uncle Perk removed the cork from the jug, and it passed solemnly from lip to lip. Mr. MacNab took a small harmonica from his pocket and sounded the key. "Happy bairthday to us," he began, "happy bairthday to us . . ."

The other members placed their arms around one another's shoulders and bent their heads together. "Happy birthday, dear Lower Forty," they sang, "happy birthday to us."

The whole club joined in close harmony, with the exception of Cousin Sid. He was busy washing the cake dishes.

Seat of Justice

Judge Parker's brow was beaded as he shouldered hastily into his judicial robes. His August court session had fallen on the very afternoon that the Lower Forty Shooting, Angling and Inside Straight Club was planning its annual bass-fishing excursion and cookout at Beaver Meadow, and only the Judge's heartfelt pleas had persuaded his fellow members to postpone their departure until his official duties were over.

"I won't be long," he assured them, pulling the loose black gown over his canvas fishing jacket and hooking the collar to conceal the red bandanna at his neck. "All I've got to do is pass sentence on Hentracks Hennessy."

"What's Hentracks up for?" asked Doc Hall.

"Assault and battery and creating a disturbance of the peace and driving his poor wife out into the rain." The Judge gathered his lawbooks under an arm, slung his creel over his shoulder and led the way out of his private chambers. "If there's anything I hate, it's a wife beater," he said grimly, "particularly in bass season."

He clumped across the courtroom, the long robe flapping around his rubber boots, and dumped the lawbooks on the bench and stowed his fishing gear carefully behind it. The other members of the Lower Forty seated themselves at the rear of the room, and the Judge rapped for order. "Now then, Hentracks," he said briskly, "you got anything to say in your own defense?"

"He ain't got any defense, Judge," Mrs. Hennessy interrupted from the other side of the courtroom. "He hit me with a canoe paddle and . . ."

Judge Parker held up his hand. "The court sympathizes with you, Myra," he said gently, "but in all justice we must let this lowdown, good-for-nothing husband of yours speak for himself." He glowered at the culprit over his spectacles. "I intend to give you a fair trial before I jail you. Just wotinell did you hit your wife for?"

"Wal, your honor," Hentracks sighed, "it's a long story."

"Cut it short," the Judge ordered, glancing at the clock on the wall. "This court has some very important business as soon as I've finished sentencing you."

The defendant licked his lips nervously. "The way it all started," he began, "I was rummaging through my freezer down in the cellar the other day, and I come acrost one last package of venison that was left over from my two hundred-pound buck I got last fall. Natchally I re'lized I didn't have no legal right to keep the meat this late in the year," he explained with a guilty look at Owl Eyes Osborn, the conservation officer, "so I decided to make a venison stew, because they ain't nothing I like better than a good stew, except I like to make it myself, because you know how it is, your honor, a woman don't know how to make a venison stew right."

"That's true," Judge Parker admitted. "They never put in enough onions."

"You need lots of onions," Hentracks agreed, "and butter, of course, and flour, and some beef stock, and peppercorns, and bay leaf . . ."

"And half a cup of lemon juice," Cousin Sid suggested from the rear of the room. "That makes all the difference."

"And a few cloves," Colonel Cobb offered. "I always put cloves in mine."

"I got to remember that," Hentracks said appreciatively and resumed. "So I mixed everything all together, and cooked it a couple of hours, and I added jes' a mite of wine to the gravy, and then at the last minute I dropped in some potato dumplings, and I tell you, Judge, it would have made your mouth drool. My wife Myra don't like venison, so she'd made herself an omelet, which meant I had the whole stew for myself, and we was really a happy family and the very pitcher of domestic bliss as we sat down to the table together. Wal, I took a little taste of the stew, and I decided it needed another dash of pepper and mebbe jes' a soopson more salt, so I reached for a pair of salt and pepper shakers I always use that are made up to look like shotgun shells . . ."

"I've got a pair just like them," Judge Parker said with growing interest. "They never plug up."

"That's why I always use 'em," Hentracks said. "The holes are big enough for the salt to come out when you want salt, so I reached for 'em, your honor, and—" he paused a moment —"and they wa'n't there. No, sir, my wife she'd threw them out, and in place of them she had a pair of antique cut-glass salt and pepper shakers she'd bought at an antique show. You know those little dinky kind?"

The Judge nodded. "My wife goes in for antiques too," he sighed, and gazed at Mrs. Hennessy reprovingly.

"So I picked up this little cut-glass saltcellar and I shook it, but nothing come out, so I shook it harder and still nothing come, so I turned it upside down and hit it with the palm of my hand, and the top come off and dumped the whole shakerful into my lovely stew and ruint it, and they wa'n't no more venison till next fall. And with that I jumped up from the table and grabbed my .410, and I opened the front door and threw the cut-glass saltcellar as high as I could into the air, and I nailed it with the right barrel as it come down, and then I threw the pepper shaker into the air and unlatched the left barrel and ground it into powdered glass—"

Judge Parker cocked his ears. "How is your .410 bored?"

"Full and full, your honor. It's the last of them wonderful old Parkers that they stopped production on after the war. It was rigged on special order with semibeavertail fore end and single trigger."

"What load were you using?" Cousin Sid inquired.

"Wal, I started to load with 7½, and then I decided if I really wanted to dust that goldang saltcellar I'd better use No. 6 chilled."

"Very sound," the Judge beamed. "Very sound."

"Look here," Mrs. Hennessy broke in impatiently, "I come to this court to get justice, not to hear a lot of silly talk about guns."

Judge Parker stiffened. "Woman, guard your tongue," he warned, "or your name will be a byword and a hissing." He turned to the defendant. "Go on, Hentracks."

"Wal, with that my wife let out a bellow like a bull with a hot pitchfork stuck in its rear, and she run upstairs to my gun room and grabbed my favorite four-ounce, split-bamboo rod that's got jes' the right action, your honor, that rod would put a dry fly clear acrost a brook and lay it onto the water slick as you'd want to see—"

"That's the kind I like," Doc Hall agreed enthusiastically. "Stiff enough but not too stiff."

"—and she took it in her both hands and laid the tip acrost her knee, and she smashed it to smithereens." His voice broke, and he controlled himself with an effort. "So with that I run up to the gun room and got my canoe paddle, and my wife seen me coming and started for the door, and I made one big swipe and caught her on the rump and boosted her halfway down the front walk."

The courtroom was silent as he finished. "Lemme see that

paddle," said Owl Eyes, picking up the evidence and examining it with a professional eye. "Yessir, Judge, there's a split right here in the blade where it collided with her fanny." He handed the paddle to Judge Parker. "Why, if Hentracks was to use that paddle in fast water and mebbe hit a rock, it would bust clean in two and prob'ly upset the canoe."

The Judge leveled an accusing forefinger at Mrs. Hennessy. "Do you realize that your carelessness might have caused your husband to get drowned or suffer even more serious injury?"

"Carelessness!" Mrs. Hennessy gasped, springing to her feet. "Why, that brute deliberately assaulted me. I got bruises and welts all over me to prove it."

"This court does not admit evidence by testimony when it is available for direct visual examination," Judge Parker announced, "and you needn't use any false plea of modesty with me, either, because what the females are wearing for bathing suits these days has destroyed modesty and damn near ruined the textile industry. If you've got any bruises, you can show them here and now, or I'll have to render a verdict of not guilty for the defendant."

"I'll do no such thing," Mrs. Hennessy bristled, her cheeks reddening, "and you can render any verdict you've a mind to."

"In that case," said the Judge, "I hereby sentence the complainant to pay for damages to the canoe paddle. And what's more," he added quickly as Mrs. Hennessy opened her mouth to protest, "the complainant is warned to depart quietly, because it would be just as easy for me to say ten days for contempt." He rapped the gavel. "This setting of court is hereby adjourned."

Judge Parker waited until the courtroom door slammed behind Mrs. Hennessy. He yanked off his black robe with relief, gathered up his fishing gear and beckoned to the other members to follow him. Hentracks Hennessy was lingering in the doorway.

"By the way, Hentracks," the Judge suggested, "why don't you come along to Beaver Meadow this afternoon for our cookout? We've got some venison meat we've been saving up all year, and maybe you could show us how you made that stew."

Buster's Bedtime Bear

Something had to be done, all the members of the Lower Forty Shooting, Angling and Inside Straight Club agreed. The bears around Hardscrabble were on the increase and getting bolder every day. Evidently a lack of natural food had brought them down from the hills, and the hungry creatures were invading the farms on the very outskirts of town, raiding orchards and marauding livestock.

"On'y last night one of 'em got into the Widow Libbey's flock of sheep," Uncle Perk reported, "and made off with a young lamb. The poor lady's scairt to death it will be back again tonight."

"Let's get out and wait for it," Judge Parker said promptly. "We'll nail it when it shows up."

" 'Taint as easy as that," Uncle Perk pointed out. "Bears is mighty smart. Why, a coupla years ago my Cousin Egbert had a bear git into his barnyard and lug off one of his prize shoats. Cousin Egbert sat up all the next night with his rifle, but that bear waited till pitch blackness and then grabbed another shoat right under Egbert's nose, and he couldn't even see to fire. So the next night Egbert figgers to outsmart him by leavin' a lighted lantrun in the barn.

"Sure enough, along about midnight he hears a big catouse, and a shoat squealin', and he grabs his rifle and runs out, and there's Mr. Bear strollin' off acrost the barnyard, holdin' the shoat under one arm and carryin' the lantrun with the other. Wal, Cousin Egbert lifts his rifle and takes careful aim, but just then the bear looks back over his shoulder, as Egbert is about to squeeze, and he lifts the lantrun quick and *ka-foo!* he blows out the light." Uncle Perk shook his head. "So it's like I say—if you want to git a bear you got to be smarter'n the bear is."

"The best plan is to surround him," Doc Hall proposed. "If we all take stands around the Libbey farm tonight..."

"I'm afraid you'll have to count me out," Colonel Cobb said regretfully. "Some friends of mine in Maine left their little son with me for a few days while they're down in the city. Buster's only fourteen, and I'd be afraid to leave the little youngster alone in the house all night."

Doc Hall's face fell. "We need every member to circle the farm," he urged. "Think of the satisfaction of doing a good deed for that poor widow...."

"Not to mention the added satisfaction of a cash r-r-remuner-r-ration from the state," Mr. MacNab added.

"Why don't you hire old Mrs. Tillinghast to come over and baby-sit tonight while you're gone?" Cousin Sid suggested to the Colonel. "She's very good with children."

Colonel Cobb hesitated. "Do you think little Buster would be perfectly safe?"

"Mrs. Tillinghast used to be a child psychologist," Cousin Sid assured him. "She'll take good care of him."

Mrs. Tillinghast exuded confidence that night as Colonel Cobb took his rifle from the gun cabinet in the front hall. "Now, don't you worry about a thing, Colonel," she beamed, patting Buster on the head with a maternal smile. "Buster and I'll have a fine time sitting together in front of the fire and playing slapjack."

"How about a little stud poker?" Buster muttered. "No limit and deuces wild."

"Isn't he cute?" Mrs. Tillinghast chuckled pleasantly. "I'll have to send that one in to Linkletter."

Colonel Cobb gave the youngster an uneasy glance as he closed the front door behind him.

Mrs. Tillinghast clasped her pudgy hands and led Buster back to the living room. "I tell you what we'll do, dear," she smiled. "If you're a good boy, I'll read you a chapter of *Black Beauty* before you go to sleep."

"Happen to have a copy of *Field & Stream* handy?" Buster asked. "I'd like to hear what Warren Page has to say about handloads."

Ignoring him, Mrs. Tillinghast settled herself comfortably

in a rocking chair before the hearth, adjusted her spectacles, and began reading aloud. She was halfway through the chapter before she realized that Buster had disappeared. After a nervous search, she located him in the front hall, taking out the contents of the Colonel's gun cabinet and examining them one by one. She caught her breath as he lifted a rifle to his shoulder. "Put that gun down! It might go off."

"Shucks, lady," Buster shrugged, "this old Springfield sporter couldn't go off. The bolt's open and there's nothing in the magazine or chamber."

He laid his cheek to the stock with professional ease, sighted along it and caressed the trigger with his forefinger. Mrs. Tillinghast held her ears.

"Not a bad piece," he commented, setting it back in the cabinet. "My old man has one just like it. I made a three-inch group with it the other day at a hundred yards." He peered at another rifle. "Well, if here isn't a genuine old .33 Winchester Model 86...."

Mrs. Tillinghast licked her lips. "It's getting late, dear," she said. "I think it's time for beddy-by."

"I don't feel like turning in yet," Buster objected, following her into the living room. "I want to catch *Gunsmoke* on TV at ten."

"You'd better go to bed right away," Mrs. Tillinghast warned, "or that big bad bear will come and eat you up."

"What bear?" Buster asked with a skeptical frown.

"The one out there in the orchard behind the house," Mrs. Tillinghast said, lowering her voice. "I saw it through the window just now, so you'd better get under the covers right away."

"Is it a big bear?" inquired Buster with interest.

Mrs. Tillinghast pretended to shiver. "It's the biggest I ever saw," she insisted. "It's got long claws and great big sharp teeth to bite you with, if you're not a good boy." She peered at Buster's thoughtful expression. "Now, you run along and get undressed, and I'll come up later and tuck you in."

Buster hurried out of the living room, and Mrs. Tillinghast settled back in her rocking chair before the fire, smiling to herself as she opened her knitting bag. After all, she reflected contentedly, you have to use a little child psychology sometimes. Then, just as she took out a ball of yarn, a deafening *ka-pow! ka-pow! ka-pow!* sounded in the yard. Mrs. Tillinghast's rocking chair came forward with a jolt, her knitting needles flew into the air and the ball of yarn rolled under the sofa. A fourth *ka-pow!* made the windows rattle, and she sprang to her feet and raced to the foot of the stairs. "Buster!" she screamed. "Are you all right?"

There was no answer. She galloped upstairs to Buster's bedroom, but it was empty. With a gasp of alarm she started back downstairs, shouting, "Buster, where are you?"

"Right here," Buster answered, strolling nonchalantly through the door with the Winchester 86 hooked over his forearm. "I figured these open sights would be better at night," he explained. He yanked down the lever, caught the last live round in midair and set the rifle back in the gun cabinet. Humming to himself, he picked up the phone. "Operator," he said, "give me the nearest garage."

"Buster," Mrs. Tillinghast stammered, "wh—what happened?"

Buster held up a hand for silence. "Look, will you send over a wrecker to Colonel Cobb's house right away? I've got a three hundred-pound bear I got to hoist up and clean."

"Bear?" Mrs. Tillinghast echoed faintly. She forced a smile. "It's just your imagination!"

"Imagination, hell," said Buster, leading her to the window and aiming a six-cell flashlight at the orchard. "You never saw imagination lying on the ground and leaking blood all over the grass, did you?"

Mrs. Tillinghast's eyes glazed as she stared at the prostrate carcass under an apple tree, and her body stiffened. She began to sway slightly, emitting a low, vibrant moan.

"I'll use a washtub to catch the guts and gurry," Buster began, strapping Colonel Cobb's hunting knife to his belt. "You can hold the flashlight when I start gutting him. . . ."

There was a faint thud. Mrs. Tillinghast lay sprawled on the floor. Buster glanced at her, picked up the phone and called the garage again. "Look, when you send that wrecker to Colonel Cobb's house," he said, "you'd better send along a doctor, too."

Doc Hall, summoned from his stand at the Libbey farm by a state trooper, braked his car in Colonel Cobb's yard and raced into the house. The other members of the Lower Forty halted and stared dumfounded at the scene in the Colonel's orchard. A huge bear dangled from the crane on the wrecker, and little Buster, stripped to the waist, was busily cleaning the carcass. Colonel Cobb studied four neat holes in the hide.

"Slammed three rounds into the body, and then a safety shot

to the head," Buster told him casually over a shoulder. "If he hadn't folded, I'd have gone around behind him to see what was holding him up."

Doc Hall emerged from the house. "Mrs. Tillinghast will be all right," he reported. "I gave her a sedative and put her to bed for the night." He glanced at his watch. "We've still got time to get back to the Widow Libbey's in case another bear shows up tonight."

"I don't know about leaving Mrs. Tillinghast alone in the house," Colonel Cobb hesitated.

"Reckon she'll be perfectly safe," Uncle Perk mused. "Little Buster'll take good care of her."

Puppy Love

The strap of sleigh bells inside Uncle Perk's front door jangled, and the members of the Lower Forty Shooting, Angling and Inside Straight Club looked up hopefully as Doc Hall shuffled into the store. Doc met their inquiring glances and shook his head in silence. "No news," he reported, and plumped despondently onto a stack of flour bags beside the potbellied stove. "I've scoured every inch of Hardscrabble and most of the back country around, I've whistled and hollered till I'm hoarse," he sighed, "but nary a sign of that little pup. Sure beats me where he could be."

His fellow members clucked in sympathy. Three days had passed since Doc Hall's six-month-old pointer, a son of old Timberdoodle, had wriggled through a half-open window of the car and disappeared, and all efforts to locate him had been in vain. "Right at the start of bird season, too," Doc added. "I'd been planning to work him with Timmy this fall, so he could pick up a few of his old man's tricks."

"He's bound to show up," Cousin Sid said reassuringly, but without conviction. "A puppy his age couldn't stray far."

Judge Parker frowned. "Maybe he didn't stray," he suggested darkly. "A nice-looking young pointer like that would be quite a temptation for some low-down hunter to steal."

"That's why I ran this little notice in today's *Gazette*," Colonel Cobb said, handing the newspaper to Doc. "The culprit might bring him back if he thought there'd be a reward."

"Aye, mon," Mr. MacNab agreed, "there's nothing more per-r-r-suasive than guid har-r-rd cash."

Doc Hall's eyes narrowed. "Any man that'd steal a bird dog," he said between his teeth, "is somebody I'd like to get a good look at, preferably through the 2½-power on my .30–06. . . .'"

He paused as a pickup truck rattled to a halt outside the store. A gaunt farmer in faded dungarees clambered out of the cab and strode through the door, clanging the sleigh bells. He scanned the group dourly. "Any you fellers lost a dog?" he asked.

Doc Hall's face tightened. "I did."

"Wal, I got him," the stranger replied tersely. Without another word he turned and strode back to the truck and opened the cab door. "Bring him in, Jerry," he said.

Doc Hall's grim expression changed to surprise as a skinny

youngster of ten clambered out of the cab and carried the missing pointer into the store. The puppy was cradled upside down in the boy's arms, his long legs dangling loosely, and now and then he reached up and lapped the youngster's freckled face with a long red tongue. The boy halted before Doc Hall, and his lower lip wobbled.

"Take him, mister," he said, his eyes welling with tears. "He's yourn."

Doc Hall took the protesting pup from the boy's embrace and turned to the older man. "Well, I'm very much obliged, Mr.—"

"Flint's the name. Eben Flint. I live over to Skunk Hollow."

"Is that where your son found him?"

"Jerry didn't find him," Eben Flint said. "The dog found Jerry. He followed the boy home from school, and kep' taggin' after him and waggin' his tail and tryin' to climb up in his lap and kiss him. So as soon as I seen the ad in the paper today I made Jerry bring him back."

Doc Hall reached for his wallet. "Well, I'd like to offer you a little something for all your trouble."

"I don't want no reward," Eben Flint said stubbornly. "I'm on'y too glad to get rid of him."

Doc's wallet halted in mid-air, and he echoed incredulously, "Glad to get rid of him?"

"That's right," Eben Flint nodded. "I don't approve of a boy having a dog."

There was a sharp gasp as the members of the Lower Forty caught their breath in unison.

Eben faced the group defiantly. "A dog's a waste of time," he insisted. "Takes a boy's mind off'n his schoolwork and chores. He's allus feedin' him or playin' with him or somepin when he'd ought to be doing more important things . . ."

"Tell me, Mr. Flint," Judge Parker interrupted in a strangled voice, "did you ever have a dog when you were a boy?"

"Not me," Eben replied. "My daddy wouldn't let me, and I ain't a-gonna let my son neither." He turned on his heel. "Come along, Jerry."

The puppy wriggled out of Doc Hall's arms and ran to Jerry. The boy dropped on his knees and buried his face in the soft furry neck, his shoulders shaking convulsively. Doc watched uneasily.

"Naow, jest a minute, Eben," Uncle Perk murmured, packing tobacco intently into his battered corncob. "They's dogs and then they's dogs. I was jest wonderin' if you ever gunned for pa'tridge, f'rinstance?"

Eben Flint hesitated. "Oh, I might knock the head off'n one, if I see it in the road," he admitted. "They make mighty good eatin', but they're pretty scarce to find."

"Then you ain't never seen a bird dog point a pa'tridge?" Uncle Perk asked, rasping a match across the scarred desk top.

Eben shook his head skeptically. "I heerd tell about sech things, but I never really believed it."

"Wal, naow, it jest so happens we was planning a little bird hunt this afternoon"—Uncle Perk peered significantly at the other members over the flare of the match—"so why don't you come along and watch Doc's dog? Might be you could shoot yourself a nice fat pa'tridge for supper."

"I ain't tasted one in a long time," Eben admitted. "Okay, if it don't take too long." He said to Jerry, "You wait here."

Uncle Perk glanced at the boy's stricken face and exhaled a

cloud of tobacco smoke. "Doc's dog is bringin' his puppy along," he suggested. "Why don't you bring your own young'un to keep him company?"

The October afternoon was sharp, and the aroma of matted leaves and rotting wild apples filled the air as the members followed Timberdoodle through the alder patch at the bottom of the Libbey lower forty. Eben Flint watched in growing admiration as Timmy quartered the cover expertly, making long casts into the wind, trailing each filament of scent. Jerry and the little pup brought up the rear of the group; whenever they halted for a moment, the pup sidled against the boy's legs and Jerry reached down and fondled a long silky ear. Judge Parker nudged Doc Hall. "Looks like a real case of puppy love."

Doc nodded thoughtfully.

At the far end of the alder patch, an apple tree overhung a stone wall, surrounded by young pines. Timberdoodle approached at a steady trot and suddenly banged into a classic point, his tail high and one foreleg cocked. Doc Hall handed his shotgun to Eben Flint. "Go ahead and take it," he said.

Eben licked his lips nervously. "What do I do?"

"Walk right up on the dog. He won't move. Be ready when the bird flushes."

Eben Flint gripped the gun and started forward. As he took a step past the frozen pointer, a partridge thundered up before him. There was an even more deafening explosion, a cloud of brown feathers filled the air and the bird folded and plummeted into a blackberry thicket.

"I hit it!" Eben yelled in delight. "Somebody grab it before it gits away!"

A small white form darted past his legs and dived into the

thicket. There was a brief scuffle, and the puppy emerged, carrying the limp partridge in his jaws. The bird's big wings almost covered the little dog's face, and his eyes were barely visible above the feathered back, as he searched the crowd. He trotted past Eben, past Doc Hall, past all the others to the rear of the group. He halted before Jerry, reared on his hind legs and braced his forepaws against the boy's chest. Jerry took the bird wonderingly from his mouth.

"Looks like the pup knows who belongs to him," Uncle Perk murmured.

Eben Flint was staring at his son. His thin mouth worked, and his Adam's apple bobbed up and down a couple of times. Doc Hall caught his eye and smiled. "If you won't take a reward for the dog," he whispered, "maybe you'll take the dog for a reward."

Eben nodded and smiled back.

The members of the Lower Forty watched Eben Flint and Jerry walk back to the pickup truck, the puppy trotting at the boy's heels. "I kind of figgered ol' Eben couldn't resist it," Uncle Perk chuckled as they headed for their car, "oncet he shot a bird over a dog. The only chance we took was that he might miss it."

"There wasn't any chance of that," Judge Parker said, ejecting an empty shell from his shotgun. "I covered him by shooting the bird at the same time."

"*You* shot the bird?" gasped Cousin Sid. "Why, so did I."

"I shot too," said Colonel Cobb. "I wanted to be sure."

"If I'd known ye were all fir-r-ring," mourned Mr. MacNab, "I wouldna squandered my own pr-r-recious ammunition."

Doc Hall settled back in the rear seat of the hearse as the pickup rattled past them down the road. He had a final glimpse of a freckled face at the cab window, and a long red tongue lapping it contentedly. He looked down at old Timberdoodle, curled on the seat beside him with his jowls resting on Doc's knee. "Well, pal," he said, fondling a long silky ear, "I guess you'll have to get started on another litter as soon as bird season is over."

The Deacon Gets Lost

Owl Eyes Osborn, the local conservation officer, burst through the door of Uncle Perk's store. "Need some volunteers right away," he panted. "We're organizing a search party."

The startled members of the Lower Forty leaped to their feet. "What's happened?" Colonel Cobb asked.

"Fellow lost up on Moose Mountain," Owl Eyes answered. "Been missing since yesterday morning. I got to get some more people to help." He turned to leave. "Meet me at Cushin's Corners at the base of the mountain, and we'll work out a search pattern."

Judge Parker grabbed his hunting jacket from a peg on the wall. "By the way, who's lost?" he shouted.

"Deacon Godfrey," Owl Eyes called back as he climbed into his truck.

The Judge halted abruptly, and hung his jacket back on the peg. "That psalm-singing old hypocrite," he growled. "Let him stay lost. Whyinell would anybody want to find him?"

"But Judge, he might be in trouble," Cousin Sid urged. "It's your duty to help look for him. Suppose you were in the Deacon's place."

"If I was in his place," the Judge retorted, "I wouldn't have to look." He shouldered into his jacket reluctantly. "Why don't they use bloodhounds to trail him?" he grumbled.

"He's so par-r-rsimonious," Mr. MacNab said, "he wouldna leave a scent."

Uncle Perk took down his battered shotgun from the rack. "I'll take this along and fire it into the air for a signal."

"Fire it into the bushes," Doc Hall suggested sourly, "in case he's hiding there."

A number of other cars were parked at Cushin's Corners, and the search party was already being instructed as Mr. MacNab's hearse arrived. "We'll send one group up the ravine, and another one can work around the back side of the mountain," Owl Eyes ordered. "And remember, boys, no cigarettes. There's a fire ban on. Governor's proclamation."

Judge Parker hurried to catch up with Owl Eyes as they started to climb. "Why are you so sure the Deacon's up here?"

"He mentioned it to several people yesterday morning,"

Owl Eyes explained. "Said he was going to take a stroll up Moose Mountain and look at the view."

"The only view that old skinflint's interested in," Colonel Cobb muttered to himself, "is a good close look at the Widow Libbey's pocketbook."

Judge Parker glanced at him with interest. "What's he been up to lately?"

The Colonel halted a moment to catch his breath and mop his forehead. "I was talking with some people at the bank the other day," he explained. "Seems the bank holds a mortgage on the widow's wood lot, and the Deacon got wind of the fact that it's overdue. So he pointed out that there was a bank examination coming along shortly, and he'd be glad to help them out by taking the mortgage off their hands." Colonel Cobb shrugged. "Which means he'll get the wood lot at a quarter the value."

"Just where is this wood lot?" Judge Parker asked curiously.

"It's that sort of island in the big swamp beyond Beaver Meadow," the Colonel said. "I was hunting rabbits there a few years ago, and it's nothing but a mess of blowdowns and bog holes. Took me half a day to find my way out again."

The Judge's face had a shrewd look. "Tell me," he mused. "If you were thinking of buying a wood lot, wouldn't you want to look it over first?"

"I suppose so, sure."

"And naturally you wouldn't let anybody know you were looking at it."

"That's right," the Colonel nodded. "I'd probably tell them I was going somewhere else instead."

"Like taking a stroll up Moose Mountain to look at the view, for instance," the Judge suggested significantly.

Colonel Cobb's eyes narrowed, and the other members of the Lower Forty exchanged quick glances. The rest of the search party had moved up the trail out of sight. With one accord they turned and hurried back down the mountain to Mr. MacNab's hearse.

The road across Beaver Meadow was in poor condition, and they moved slowly through deep ruts made by previous cars. Ahead of them was a wide stretch of bottom land, flooded by beavers and dotted here and there with dead tree trunks. Judge Parker was peering at the tree-covered island in the center of the swamp, and he sat forward suddenly. "Look there!" he exclaimed. "Isn't that smoke?"

A gray cloud hovered over the island, spreading and growing thicker as they watched. Mr. MacNab sped up the hearse, and they crossed a boggy stretch and halted at a deep lake, where a beaver dam had flooded the road completely. The members climbed out and the Judge pointed in silence to Deacon Godfrey's empty car, hidden in a clump of bushes. Their eyes moved across the swamp to the billowing cloud of smoke, lashed here and there with darting red flames.

"At least it can't spread anywhere," Judge Parker said. "Nothing but water all around it."

"But what about the Deacon?" Cousin Sid gasped.

"Too hot to go in there and look for him," Doc Hall replied flatly. "Even the animals are starting to leave. There's a beaver swimming toward us right now."

Colonel Cobb shaded his eyes. "That's not a beaver," he said. "That's Deacon Godfrey."

Cousin Sid extended a hand as the Deacon floundered out of the water, trailing mud and slime, and helped him onto the bank. Deacon Godfrey's face was streaked with soot, and he choked for breath. "Thought I was a goner when that fire started spreading," he groaned.

"How did it start?" Judge Parker asked.

"I got lost in there yesterday and I had to spend the night, so I built a little smudge to keep off the mosquitoes," the Deacon told them. "And then it got out of hand and chased me right into the water." His teeth chattered. "I'm sure glad to be out of it."

"You're not out of it, Buster," the Judge said grimly, "until you pay the Widow Libbey the cost of her wood lot that you burned up."

Deacon Godfrey recoiled. "But I just cruised that whole wood lot," he protested, "and it isn't worth a cent."

"Except to the bank," the Judge reminded him. "There's nothing meaner than a New England banker when somebody burns up his equity with no insurance." He glowered over his spectacles. "Unless it's a New England conservation officer when he finds that somebody has deliberately started a fire with a woods ban on." The Judge's voice sank to an ominously low pitch. "Or maybe the meanest of all is a New England judge when somebody is hauled into his court for trespassing and arson and general highbowdjery."

The Deacon's face paled under its coating of soot, and he backed a step.

"So if I was in your room," the Judge suggested, "I'd avoid a lot of trouble by coming back to town and making out a check to the Widow Libbey right now." He followed the Deacon toward his parked car, and glanced back at the other members of the Lower Forty. "You fellows don't mind sticking around a while and making sure that fire burns itself out?"

"Oh, we don't mind a bit, Jedge," Uncle Perk assured him, taking a jug of Old Stump Blower out of the hearse. "This here's the nicest rescue I ever enjoyed."

The Wayward Hearse

Pandemonium reigned at the April meeting of the Lower Forty Shooting, Angling and Inside Straight Club. All day long the harried members had been rushing in and out of Uncle Perk's store, investigating new leads, checking rumors, reporting any bits of gossip that might offer some clue to the current mystery. Judge Parker, in his shirt sleeves, had established a command post at Uncle Perk's roll-top desk, with the telephone clamped to his ear. "Any word, Owl Eyes? Well, tell your boys to keep looking." He replaced the receiver, and the phone rang again. "That you, Woolboot? Nothing new?" The bell jangled again as he set the phone down, and he picked it up promptly. "Who? Oh, hello, Leadfoot. Okay, thanks." The Judge swiveled to face the room dejectedly. "State Trooper Langlois says he hasn't found a trace."

Doc Hall drove a fist into his cupped palm. "It's bound to show up sometime. You can't hide a hearse forever."

"Particularly a hearse like Mr. MacNab's," Colonel Cobb insisted, mopping his forehead.

His fellow members nodded in silent agreement. The Mac-Nab hearse was a very special one, fitted out with loving care to meet the piscatorial requirements of the Lower Forty. Its sides had been equipped with racks to hold their fishing rods, the body had a plywood flooring for their sleeping bags so that they could sleep inside in case of rain, and the hearse's built-in refrigerating system proved an ideal storage place to keep their trout fresh. They had even rigged it with a radio and a portable stove, which could be removed during business hours. Each spring the club set forth in this convenient vehicle for a week's fishing in Canada, in exchange for a small fee of twenty-five dollars per member that Mr. MacNab collected to reimburse him for wear and tear on the chrome trimmings and enable him to put the hearse back in shape for the summer interment season. This April they were about to start as usual on their annual jaunt when, on the very eve of their departure, the hearse mysteriously disappeared.

News of its loss had fallen like a bombshell on the Lower Forty. Only Mr. MacNab had maintained a philosophic calm at first. "Dinna fret," he assured them. "It's thorr-r-oughly covered by insur-r-rance, and I'll use the cash to pur-r-rchase a more up-to-date model, with flashing beehive light and a sir-r-ren, so I can use it for an ambulance as well."

"By the way," Judge Parker asked, "where are your insurance papers?"

"They're in the glove compar-r-rtment of my hair-r-rse . . ." Mr. MacNab's face suddenly blanched, and he emitted a loud wail of anguish. "Sound the alar-r-rm! Call out the guar-r-rds! We've got to find the thief at once!"

No stone had been left unturned in the frantic search that ensued. Owl Eyes Osborn, the local warden, had flashed the word to every wildlife agent in the state. Woolboot Jackson had ordered his fellow sheriffs to be on the lookout, and Leadfoot Langlois, the state trooper, had teletyped an alert to adjoining states. Colonel Cobb's printshop had rushed five hundred posters, to be displayed in lunchrooms and filling stations, and Uncle Perk had promised an entire case of Old Stump Blower as a reward if the culprit was apprehended. Thus far all efforts had not unearthed a single clue.

"Maybe some college boys stole it for a prank," Cousin Sid suggested. "I read in the *Times* the other day that students at Swarthmore are collecting old hearses for multiple dating and other campus activities."

Mr. MacNab shook his head. " 'Tis my theor-r-ry," he said, "that it was stolen by some r-r-rival undertaker to for-r-rce me out of business. Pairsonally I wouldna put it past my Cousin Fairgus."

"The state troopers have been stopping every hearse for the past week," Colonel Cobb pointed out. "It's getting so it isn't safe to be buried these days. Yesterday they halted three funeral processions on the turnpike and frisked the drivers. The relatives of the late lamented were quite upset."

"I understand that the State Embalmers Association is issuing special certificates of ownership," Doc Hall added, "to be pasted on the windshield in a conspicuous place."

"What I can't figure out," Cousin Sid sighed, "is how it ever got past all those roadblocks."

Judge Parker banged Uncle Perk's desk with his fist. "I've got a hunch it didn't—that it isn't very far away. Let's organize a posse and search each house in town. I'll issue the warrants myself."

Dexter Smeed shifted uncomfortably in his chair. "Now, Judge," he protested weakly, "wouldn't that be a lot of trouble?"

Judge Parker gazed at his wife's nephew with thin contempt. "If I ever catch up with that thief," he scowled, "I'll show him what trouble really is." He waved an arm at his fellow members. "Everybody show up here in an hour with his favorite weapon, and we'll take the law into our own hands."

The faces of the Lower Forty were grim as they assembled in Uncle Perk's store, bristling with armament in case the culprit offered resistance. Judge Parker brandished an old .351 Winchester automatic rifle with a pair of ten-shot clips. "If I can't serve notice on him with twenty rounds," the Judge remarked ominously, "I'll hang up my guns."

Colonel Cobb displayed a gleaming Johnson semiautomatic .30–06. "I've loaded the clips with alternate rounds of tracer and armor-piercing, in case he refuses to come out of the hearse." He glanced at Mr. MacNab's worried expression. "It'll be a personal pleasure to pay for any holes."

"Personally I don't go in for fancy new weapons in an emergency like this," Doc Hall said, reaching inside his coat and sliding out a 4¾-inch-barrel Colt Frontier. The gun was worn clean of all finish, and the ivory grips had the fine patina of age. "All I want is five seconds of his time at twenty-five yards."

Uncle Perk produced an old 10-bore Remington double, its barrels sawed back to twenty inches. "Used to belong to my great-uncle Peasley Perkins," he explained. "Peasley was comin' out of a duck marsh one night, and I guess he kinda underestimated how much Stump Blower he'd consumed, and he slipped and fell and druv ten inches of black marsh mud into the barrels, which he didn't notice at the time. Nach'ly the next time Peasley touched her off it set him flat on his fanny and took just ten inches offen them tubes, so he give her to me. I'm usin' a handful of 00 buck in each barrel."

Mr. MacNab held up a fine old .50–70 Sharps carbine with a belt of fresh black-powder reloads, and weighed a cartridge in the palm of his hand. "'Tis how Winchester-r-r used to load their old .50–110 Expr-r-ress," he told the others. "Ye just tap a quar-r-rter-inch hole in the nose o' the bullet and put in a wee drap o' glue, and pr-r-ress in a .22 blank." His eyes had a vengeful light. "Aye, 'tis verra, verra lovely when it hits."

Dexter Smeed's gaze moved slowly from weapon to lethal weapon and his face turned a pale sea green. He licked his lips. "Look, could I speak to you a moment?" he murmured to Mr. MacNab. "Let's step out in back."

Puzzled, Mr. MacNab followed Dexter into the storeroom at the rear. Dexter closed the door and lowered his voice. "It's —it's about your hearse," he whispered. "I know where it is."

"Why dinna ye say so?" Mr. MacNab gasped.

"I didn't want Judge Parker to hear," Dexter placed his lips close to Mr. MacNab's ear. "It's in the back of the Judge's barn, covered over with an old tarpaulin and several bales of hay."

"Why, that no-guid, thieving magistr-r-rate!" Mr. MacNab exclaimed. "So *he's* the guilty one!"

"Oh, the Judge didn't steal it," Dexter confessed unhappily. "I did." He held up a hand in defense as Mr. MacNab advanced on him, and added quickly, "I had a date to take out that pretty schoolteacher, the one Deacon Godfrey's been courting lately, and I figured nobody would think of looking inside a hearse if it was parked in the moonlight; so I borrowed it just for the night. Then, when all the excitement started, I was afraid to bring it back, and I hid it in the Judge's barn. You won't tell him?"

Mr. MacNab beamed with pleasure. "Why, Dex, old mon," he chortled, "anybody who'd take Deacon Godfrey's gur-r-rl away from him desairves a gold medal, at least." A familiar sly look came over his face. "I tell ye what I'll do. If ye'll give me the sum of a hundred and fifty dollar-r-rs in har-r-rd cash, representing the amount of twenty-five dollar-r-rs each member was planning to pay me for the use of my hair-r-rse, ye can leave the vehicle in front of Uncle Pairk's store at midnight, and I'll never br-r-reathe a word to the Judge."

Next morning Mr. MacNab watched patiently as the members stored their fishing gear in the recovered hearse. So over-joyed were they at the return of the club transportation in perfect condition that they did not ask any questions. He waited until they had climbed aboard, and cleared his throat. "Before we star-r-rt," he reminded them, "there's a wee matter of twenty-five dollar-r-rs apiece ye owe me."

Dexter Smeed's jaw sagged, and he stared in bewilderment as each member paid his fee in turn. Mr. MacNab halted in front of him, and he stammered, "But—but I thought—I mean, you said . . ."

Mr. MacNab was smiling a fixed smile. Dexter's eyes moved to Judge Parker, and his protests faded into silence. With a sigh of resignation he placed another twenty-five dollars in the outstretched hand before him.

"Now, ther-r-re's just one more sma' matter to be settled," Mr. MacNab added, folding the bills into his already bulging wallet. " 'Tis my recollection that Uncle Perk offered a case of Old Stump Blower if the culprit was appr-r-rehended. Since we dinna ken the thief, I move that this generous r-r-reward be donated to the club for our coming trip."

His smile broadened as Uncle Perk headed back, grumbling, into the store. "Take it all in all," Mr. MacNab murmured, "it's been a most satisfactor-r-ry theft."

The Prize Sucker

The members of the Lower Forty Shooting, Angling and Inside Straight Club were in a disgruntled mood at their May meeting. "Not that I object if the women want to put on a church supper," Judge Parker said, "to make some money for a new gas stove for the parish house. What I want to know is how they're going to make any money if the food costs more than the tickets."

"I asked my wife the same question," Doc Hall sighed, "but she said the Ladies Club decided they really couldn't charge more than a dollar a plate, so their husbands would have to make up the deficit."

"A dollar for a meal like *this?*" Cousin Sid marveled, reading the proposed menu aloud. "Chicken pie, baked ham, roast turkey, choice of salad, Parker House rolls, six kinds of pie, and all the coffee you can drink. Do you know how much that would cost you in the city?"

"What wor-r-ries me," Mr. MacNab groaned, "is how much it will cost me right here."

"It's sheer extravagance," Colonel Cobb stated flatly. "Personally I think it's high time we returned to the simple standards of our forefathers."

Uncle Perk knocked out his pipe. "Yes, sir, back in them ole days when they put on a church supper in the spring, it was somethin' wholesome and nourishin', and nobody got the seat of his pants burnt payin' for it. Like f'rinstance, the menfolks would go out and spear a mess o' suckers ..."

"Suckers?" Cousin Sid gasped, swallowing hard.

"That's right," Uncle Perk nodded. "They'd bake 'em in a bean pot with pork and onions, and jes' a little mite o' vinegar to melt the bones, and they'd cook up some danderline greens they dug on the church lawn, and for dessert they'd be baked Indian pudding with shaved maple sugar on top. I tell you, boys, there was a meal what would stick to the ribs, let alone the fac' that the whole thing didn't cost a cent except the vinegar."

Judge Parker banged the counter with his fist. "That's it! We'll all go out and spear some suckers in Swasey Pond tonight," he announced, "and put on a real old-fashioned feed like our forefathers used to."

Cousin Sid looked a trifle green. "Sucker spearing doesn't sound much like sport," he protested vaguely.

"We could get up a club pool," the Judge suggested, "and the biggest fish of the night takes the prize. That ought to stimulate competition."

"And jes' to stimulate it some more," Uncle Perk offered, "I'll contribute some o' my special hard cider I been workin' on all winter, which is well fortified with sugar and raisins, and is not to be took in the spirit of levity, but is intended to refresh us from our arduous labors."

"Now that ye put it that way, Uncle Pairk," said Mr. Mac-Nab, his eyes gleaming with anticipation, "it sounds like a verra spor-r-rting pr-r-roposition."

The gleam in Mr. MacNab's eyes faded that evening as he tasted Uncle Perk's special hard cider. He passed the jug silently to Judge Parker, who took a long swig and frowned. "No kick to this stuff at all, Uncle Perk," the Judge grumbled. "You don't happen to have some Old Stump Blower?"

"Give it time," Uncle Perk replied serenely as the circle of members sampled the cider one by one. "It's got quite a h'ist, onct it sets to workin'." He pointed to a couple of ancient dories pulled up on the shore of Swasey Pond. "I got a jug for each boat," he said, "so let's get started and mebbe it'll catch up with us."

In the bow of each dory was a car battery hooked up to an

electric light bulb. Each bulb was fastened inside an inverted dishpan that served as a reflector. Judge Parker took his place as bowman in the first boat, with Uncle Perk and Dexter Smeed behind him, and Cousin Sid at the oars. Doc Hall balanced on the thwarts of the second dory, brandishing a twelve-foot pole with a set of sharp prongs fastened at the end. "Avast, me hearties," he called over his shoulder to Colonel Cobb and Mr. MacNab. "Man the galleys and forward to the fray!"

The spirits of the members brightened perceptibly as the pair of dories circled the pond, and the bowmen began to spear the shadowy shapes that swirled under the lighted dishpans. The two sucker pails were filling fast, and the two jugs were emptying even faster. "Either tha' cider's beginnina take holt," Judge Parker observed a little thickly, "or Cousin Sid's rowing in circles."

"I thou' *you* were rowing," Cousin Sid mumbled.

Doc Hall, teetering in the bow of the other dory, made a deft lunge, then tossed a slithery object over his shoulder toward the stern. Mr. MacNab deposited the sucker in the pail, took another swig from the jug between his knees and passed it forward to Colonel Cobb. The Colonel wiped his lips and bent again manfully to the oars.

"Row, row, row y'r boat, gen'ly downa stream," he sang as they zigzagged back and forth across the pond. "Mer'ly, mer'ly, mer'ly, mer'ly . . ."

"Ship ahoy!" Doc Hall shouted as the first dory loomed in their path. "Strike the Jolly Roger, mates!" He braced himself in the bow, his spear poised. "Be prepared for boarding."

As the dories came abreast he drove his spear at the foe. There was a heavy splintering of wood, and Doc staggered backward and sat down hard in Colonel Cobb's lap.

A howl rose from the other boat. "Ye dern fool," Uncle Perk yelled, "ye put a hole right through the side."

"Water's coming in fast," Cousin Sid warned. "Dexter, start bailing."

"Life is burradream," Colonel Cobb sang, rowing mer'ly on his way.

Dexter Smeed was working feverishly in the stern of the foundering dory. Judge Parker glanced back at him and caught his breath. "Wotinell are you using to bail with, Dexter?"

"The pail the suckers were in."

"Where are the suckers?"

"I tossed 'em overboard," Dexter panted, "so I could use the pail."

Judge Parker lifted his spear and advanced on his wife's nephew threateningly. "Never mind, Judge," Cousin Sid intervened hastily as the water rose around his knees. "They've got a whole pailful in the other boat. We better get ashore before we have to swim."

The second dory was making a series of figure eights around the pond, and Colonel Cobb's voice rose above the thrashing of the oars: "Mer'ly, mer'ly, mer'ly, mer'ly." Doc Hall was asleep, his head pillowed in the Colonel's lap, and Mr. MacNab had taken his place in the bow. He peered intently at the water. "Hold it, Colonel!" he screamed. "Luik there, quick!"

Humming to himself, Colonel Cobb leaned over the side and stared where Mr. MacNab pointed, the dory canting at a perilous angle. A dark shape flashed in the light of the dishpan, and Mr. MacNab made a wild lunge. There was a resounding splash, and Colonel Cobb's song ended abruptly in a gurgle. He rose sputtering in four feet of water, holding the slumbering Doc by the scruff of his neck. Mr. MacNab emerged on the other side of the capsized dory, balancing a large, heavy object on the end of his spear. "I skewer-r-red him," he announced triumphantly. " 'Tis the world's r-r-record sucker, at least."

Colonel Cobb ignored him and waded toward shore, dragging Doc and the dory behind him.

"Wait a minute, mon," Mr. MacNab called after him. "Let's compare mine with all the others."

"What others?" asked Colonel Cobb, pointing to the empty sucker pail settling slowly underwater.

The club members sprawled disconsolately on the bank, dripping slime and shivering in the gray dawn. "What I'd give right now," Judge Parker recalled, his teeth chattering, "for a nice hot meal of chicken pie and baked ham and roast turkey and six kinds of pie and all the coffee I could drink."

"The wair-r-rst of it is," Mr. MacNab moaned, "we canna tell which is the biggest sucker of the night."

"Ef you was to ast me," Uncle Perk said briefly, "we all are."

Doc Hall roused himself and peered at the end of Mr. MacNab's spear. "That's no sucker, anyway. That's a lake trout."

"A tr-r-rout, d'ye say?" Mr. MacNab exclaimed in delight. "It must go twenty pounds, including the spear. Why, a fine tr-r-rophy like that desair-r-rves to be mounted." He pried it admiringly off the prongs. "I can stuff these holes with wax so they willna show, and put a Number-r-r Sixteen Cahill in its jaw and hang it over the mantel." His face broke into a broad smile. "I'll send for a buik on taxidair-r-rmy in the morning."

A Lesson in Taxidair-r-rmy

"Aye, the cheapest thing about a world-record tr-r-rout is catching it," Mr. MacNab sighed as he led the other members of the Lower Forty Shooting, Angling and Inside Straight Club into his dining room. " 'Tis when ye seek to presair-r-r-ve it for poster-r-rity that the r-r-real expense begins."

Judge Parker scowled at the dining-room table, littered with catalogues and instruction manuals. "Thought you invited us here tonight for supper," he grumbled.

"Dinna fr-r-r-et, Judge, Maggie is busy in the kitchen pr-r-repairing a r-r-r-epast," Mr. MacNab assured him. "But meantime, I thought ye'd like to give me a hand with my fair-r-rst lesson, which just ar-r-rived today."

Doc Hall glanced at a typewritten letter on top of the pile.

" 'Dear Student,' " he read aloud, " 'our records show that you are thirteen years of age and have your parents' consent to take this course' . . ."

"I'll admit I prevair-r-ricated a wee bit about my age," Mr. MacNab admitted sheepishly, "but there's a special cut rate for junior members."

"With all your experience in the embalmin' business," Uncle Perk grunted, "I don't see why you need any lessons in stuffin' a fish."

"Taxidair-r-rmy is an art," Mr. MacNab replied coldly, "requir-r-ring both skill and imagination." He opened a catalogue and pointed to a series of sample illustrations, showing a bride and a groom squirrel being married by a chipmunk, a pair of rabbits playing pool, an owl book end and a complete combo orchestra of stuffed frogs led by a turtle with a baton. "The problem is to make the specimen luik r-r-realistic."

"In that case," Colonel Cobb suggested, "why don't you mount it on the end of a ten-prong spear, with an empty sucker pail and a broken oar handle?"

Mr. MacNab ignored him. "I have thought of displaying it curved in a mighty leap—" his eyes lighted—"with a 4X leader and a No. 16 dry fly in its jaw. To make it even more convincing," he added, "I'll put the side with the spear holes next to the plank."

Cousin Sid was browsing through the catalogue. "There's a lot of special equipment you're going to need," he observed, his eye moving down the long list of taxidermist supplies. " 'Bone snips, cartilage knife, forceps, scalpel, bird stuffer, fat scraper, stuffing needles, ear spoon, hacksaw' . . ."

"I've got the hacksaw," Mr. MacNab said, "and I can borrow the other items from Doc Hall's sur-r-rgical kit."

"You'll want a complete assortment of glass eyes, of course," Cousin Sid continued, perusing the catalogue. " 'Deer, alligator, barred owl, coyote, cormorant, house cat, snake, sheep or goat and multicolor fish with black irregular pupils, iris beautifully colored, specially made in our own eye factory with natural blue-glint pupils, $1.85 a pair.' "

Mr. MacNab winced. "In the inter-r-rests of economy," he decided quickly, "I'll mount my tr-r-rophy with its eyes closed in blissful r-r-repose."

"Well, let's get started," the Judge said briskly. "Where's the trout?"

"Oh, it's safe downstairs in my fr-r-r-eezer," Mr. MacNab explained. "I've tr-r-raced the exact size on this piece of wrapping paper, adding only a few inches in length and a couple in gairth, which, after all, is a fisherman's pr-r-rerogative." He turned the pages of instruction manual to Lesson One. "The fairst step," he began, "is to cut a pine boar-r-rd in the shape of the body."

Humming quietly, Mr. MacNab traced the outline on a sheet of plywood, held it at arm's length and gazed thoughtfully at the result. He erased it and drew another outline a little larger. "If I'm setting a wor-r-rld record," he mused, "I might as well make it a guid one."

The other members watched in silence as he placed the piece

of plywood on the edge of the diningroom table and started to work with his hacksaw. The saw moved slower and slower, and Mr. MacNab's face grew red with effort. "I canna understand why it cuts so hard," he panted.

"Mebbe one reason," Uncle Perk murmured, "is because ye're sawin' through the table."

Mr. MacNab lifted the plywood and gazed stricken at the outline of a fish cut in his mahogany table top.

Judge Parker reached for the manual and peered at it through his spectacles. "You're doing it the hard way, Mac," he announced. "How about this hollow-body method they describe here on page a hundred and twelve?" He read the instructions. " 'Mix up a batch of papier-mâché with water into a firm paste, and spread between two sheets of cloth to form a papier-mâché sandwich.' "

"D'ye suppose that flour-and-water paste would do as well?" asked Mr. MacNab.

"Why go to all that trouble?" Doc Hall snorted in disgust. "Just skin it and stuff it like a sock."

"You could use all this sawdust on the floor," Colonel Cobb suggested, "and some old newspapers, and a little horsehair from the sofa and maybe a handful of pebbles from your wife's bowl of paper narcissus. Lake trout will swallow anything."

Mr. MacNab brightened. "A guid idea," he nooded. "I'll fetch my tr-r-rophy at once ..."

"Sorry to distair-r-rb ye, Angus," Maggie MacNab interrupted, emerging from the kitchen with an apron around her waist, "but ye'll have to clear off that table so I can set it. Supper's almost ready."

"What are we having tonight, dear?" inquired Mr. MacNab fondly.

"I was luiking through the freezer this morning and I spotted that nice fish ye caught," she told him, "so I've baked it for a surpr-r-rise."

Mr. MacNab uttered a stifled groan and collapsed on a chair. "But I was planning to have it stuffed," he moaned.

"Oh, I've seen to that, Angus," Maggie smiled. "I've pr-r-repared a fine stuffing of bread crumbs and onions and sage. I do hope ye'll all enjoy it."

Mr. MacNab's head was buried in his hands, and his downcast eyes fell on the next lesson in the instruction manual, which was entitled "Preparing the Skin." He read in a low voice. " 'Immairse in alcohol and allow to soak until thor-r-roughly pickled.' . . ." Automatically his hand reached for Uncle Perk's jug of Old Stump Blower. "Could I borrow this, Uncle Pairk?"

"Whaddye need it for?" Uncle Perk asked. "They ain't no trout to pickle."

"Who," moaned Mr. MacNab, tilting the jug to his lips, "said anything about a tr-r-rout?"

The Great Bug Safari

Uncle Perk took a .22 revolver out of his desk drawer and spun its empty cylinder with practiced fingers, his eyes fixed on a sporting-goods calendar on the opposite wall. The sheet for September showed a rather gaudy grouse poised in full flight against a tomato-colored sunset sky. Squinting over his spectacles, Uncle Perk tilted back in his swivel chair, took careful aim, pulled the trigger, and said, "Bang!"

Judge Parker strolled across the store and examined the picture critically. "Two inches to the left and a little high," he announced.

"Dang pa'tridge ducked behind a tree just as I shot," Uncle Perk complained. "And anyways, the sun was in my eyes."

"You're out of practice," the Judge said severely. "We're all out of practice, in fact." He glanced at the date on the calendar, and scowled at the other members of the Lower Forty. "Only seventeen more days left to get ready for grouse season."

"We ought to throw up some clay pigeons," Cousin Sid suggested, "to get our shooting eye in."

Doc Hall shook his head. "It isn't the same as live game. Artificial targets have their greatest speed right at the start, and slow down more and more as they fly. Wild grouse are just the opposite. Besides, a grouse doesn't always get up when you say, 'Pull.' "

"Not to mention the fr-r-rightful expense of clay bair-r-rds these days," added Mr. MacNab.

"Maybe we could try to call a few crows," suggested Colonel Cobb. "That's good practice for wing shooting."

"They won't come in any more," the Judge sighed. "They just sit in a tree and talk back. The other day I drove past some crows in a field, and they flew off before I could even hit the brakes. I think they've memorized my license plate."

"Why don't we go down to the village dump and shoot rats?" Dexter Smeed asked.

"No, that's out," Doc Hall said firmly. "My wife said the next time I came home with my clothes smelling of burnt mattress and decayed cabbage I'd have to sleep in the woodshed."

Uncle Perk reached for a jug of Old Stump Blower. "How about shooting sail cats?" he murmured.

"What's a sail cat?" inquired Mr. MacNab.

"Wal, naow, I'll tell ye," Uncle Perk explained, removing the cork. "Let's say a big ole tomcat is wanderin' down the highway on a real hot day, and a truck runs over it and a lot of other trucks keep running back and forth acrost it and fin'ly, after a coupla days, that there cat is all dried out and flatter'n a pancake. Wal, then you load your gun and you pick up that cat offen the road, and sa-a-ail it 'way high in the air." He tilted the jug and swallowed contentedly. "Ain't no better target I know of."

Mr. MacNab's gaze followed the jug longingly as Uncle Perk lowered it again, and his Adam's apple rose and fell in a convulsive gulp. "Aye, that r-r-reminds me of a tr-r-rick my grandfeyther taught me once," he began. "Fairst, ye go out on a bricht moonlicht nicht and take a shovel and gather a basketful of wild yewers . . ."

"What's yewers?" asked Uncle Perk.

"I'll have a drap of Old Stump Blower, thank ye kindly," Mr. MacNab replied promptly, as he reached for the jug. "That was the tr-r-rick my grandfeyther taught me once," he chortled.

Cousin Sid looked up from an old copy of *Field & Stream* he was reading. "Here's one way we could get some practice," he said. "We could shoot grasshoppers."

"What with?" Doc Hall asked skeptically. "A Flit gun?"

"No, you use a smooth-bore .22 rifle and ordinary .22 shot shells. Lee Wulff has an article about it here in this magazine, he says it's real sporty shooting, and calls for a lot of skill. You have to stalk them through the grass. . . ."

"Maybe you could build a blind," Judge Parker grunted, "and call them by rubbing your hind legs together."

"At least it's live game," Cousin Sid urged, "and the cost of the shells is less than two cents a shot. . . ."

"I will admit that's a verra guid ar-r-rgument," Mr. MacNab observed with new interest.

"Cousin Sid may be right," Colonel Cobb agreed. "I hear this sport of hopper-shooting is spreading all over the country. Ted Trueblood says it's so popular out in Idaho that they may have to ask the game commission to close the season on hen grasshoppers, and only shoot the cocks."

"Okay, let's give it a whirl," Judge Parker shrugged, clambering to his feet and beckoning to the others. "Coming, Uncle Perk?"

Uncle Perk shook his head. "You fellers go ahead," he muttered, flipping the page of the wall calendar to October. He peered at the illustration of a covey of bobwhite quail sailing across a bilious yellow meadow, shrugged, and settled back in his swivel chair, his revolver held in readiness. "I'll jest sit here an' wait for them pesky quail to light."

Uncle Perk shifted morosely in his chair as the other members returned late that afternoon from their safari. The quail were still sailing across the meadow, the revolver was still empty and so was the jug of Old Stump Blower. "How was *your* shootin'?" he inquired, as they strode into the store.

"You can't beat this hopper-hunting for real sport," Judge Parker reported enthusiastically. He took an empty shell box out of his pocket and dumped a pile of deceased grasshoppers on top of the showcase. "I'd have had my limit, but I ran out of ammunition."

"You think hoppers are tricky," Doc Hall said, "you ought to try hitting a darning needle." He opened a matchbox and held up a large dragonfly by its wing tips. "I led it about six inches and nailed it right through the head at thirty feet."

"Wal, naow, that's a real nice trophy, Doc," Uncle Perk remarked sarcastically. "You gonna have it mounted and hang it up?"

"Butterflies are even harder," Cousin Sid insisted, dumping the contents of his own gamebag onto the counter. "The way they zig and zag, it's worse than a woodcock in an alder thicket."

Colonel Cobb emptied out a bottleful of crickets. "Took 'em all on the hop," he insisted. "Once I even got a double."

"I dinna wish to br-r-rag," Mr. MacNab smiled, turning a sardine can upside down on the glass, "but I got thairr-r-rty-three tent caterpillars with one shot. Surpr-r-rised them in their nest," he cackled, rubbing his hands.

Judge Parker glanced at his wife's nephew. "Dexter, how did you get that big lump on your cheek?"

"I missed a hornet," Dexter Smeed sighed.

Uncle Perk strolled over to the showcase and gazed at the heap of mangled insects. He rubbed his stubbled chin thoughtfully.

"If you fellers are all through with these here trophies," he murmured, "mebbe I could borrow them for the evenin'." He scooped the pile off the counter into a bait can and started toward the door. "Seein' as how huntin' season is still a coupla weeks away," he added over his shoulder, "I think I'll go fishin'."

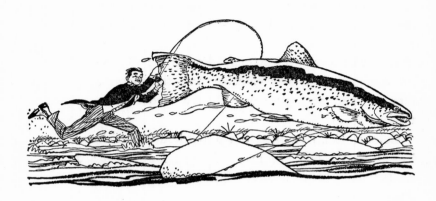

The Girl in His Life

Clad in canvas fishing jacket and waders and brandishing his aluminum rod case like a swagger stick, Colonel Cobb strode briskly into Uncle Perk's store. He stared in surprise at the other members of the Lower Forty, still wearing their business suits. "You fellows better hurry up and get ready," he remonstrated. "That evening hatch should be starting in another hour."

Judge Parker ran a finger inside his stiff white collar. "I'm afraid our fishing date is off today," he confessed uncomfortably. "Something important has just come up."

"What's more important than fishing?" Colonel Cobb demanded. "The water's just right, and as I drove into town just now I saw a couple of nice rises under the bridge. Can't you postpone your business until tomorrow?"

"It isn't business," the Judge sighed. "It's my wife. I've got to take her to the church rummage sale this afternoon."

"I'm in the same fix," Doc Hall admitted. "Jennie needs the car because she's on the refreshment committee."

"Ye'll have to count me out too," Mr. MacNab mourned. "My Maggie is going thr-r-rough our attic, picking out things for the r-r-rummage booth, and I have to be sure she doesna give away my old fishing clothes or leaky boots."

Colonel Cobb gazed at his fellow members with a superior smile. "You're tied to their apron strings, that's all," he goaded. "Why don't you assert yourselves? Tell your wives who's head of the house...."

"It's all right for a bachelor like you or Uncle Perk to talk," Judge Parker retorted. "What do you know about being married?"

"I know enough to stay single," Colonel Cobb chuckled.

"You know, Colonel, I always wondered about that," Cousin Sid remarked. "Wasn't there ever a girl in your life?"

"Well, frankly, I was engaged once," the Colonel admitted, "but the wedding was called off. It was because of Old One-Eye."

"Who was Old One-Eye?" Doc Hall asked. "The girl's mother?"

"Old One-Eye," Colonel Cobb said sternly, "was the biggest rainbow trout I ever tied into. He'd have gone five pounds, maybe six, maybe even eight or ten if I'd landed him." There was a faraway look in his eyes. "As a matter of fact, there's still a little time before the hatch starts," he offered, "in case you fellows'd like to hear about it.

"Her name was Barbara," Colonel Cobb recalled, "and she was a real nice girl, very sympathetic and understanding. Her home was in northern Michigan, but she was working in the tackle department at Abercrombie & Fitch in New York, which was how I met her. She didn't fish herself, but she just loved to hear people talk about it, she said, and she'd sit and listen to me by the hour and never interrupt once. She was just the kind of girl to take on a fishing trip; she'd patch my waders and sew the buttons on my jacket, and while I was fishing, she'd drive up and down the road beside the stream and spot new rises. Well, one thing led to another, and the first thing I knew I'd bought her an engagement ring with a big diamond, and from then on I called her Barb because she'd hooked me.

"She wanted to get married in June, but I said this interfered with the caddis hatch, so we decided on midsummer instead. Unfortunately, we had to postpone our wedding again because I got a chance to go salmon fishing on the Restigouche, and our fall plans had to be called off suddenly when I went to Alaska for the steelhead run. We set another date to get married in January, but I happened to be down in Baja California over Christmas and I got into some roosterfish, so I had to send her a cable. Did you ever cast for roosters? Best saltwater fighter I know. They'll hit a light lure and they're faster than any bonefish. Let's see. Where was I?"

"You were telling us about Barbara," said Cousin Sid.

"Oh, yes—Barb. Well, as I say, she was a very understanding girl, but this time she put her foot down. She explained that we'd been planning to get married for a whole year now, she'd waited long enough, and our wedding was going to be this coming June at her home in Michigan. I objected at first, because I hated to miss opening day back home, but she said there was good fishing in Michigan, too, and her father would give us a Jeep for a wedding present and we could spend our honeymoon exploring some of the trout streams around the peninsula. That's what I mean about being understanding.

"I got to talking to her father the night before the wedding —we had a few drinks together—and that was when he mentioned Old One-Eye. He'd been trying for that old trout for years, he said, but he'd had to give up lately because his wife objected to his going fishing all the time. He drew me a map of the stream. It was only about two hours' drive north, and he even marked the pool where Old One-Eye was. I noticed that he had a sort of glazed expression when he mentioned it, and for some reason it made me think of a stuffed trout over the mantel.

"The day of the wedding dawned bright and clear. The ceremony wasn't until three o'clock, so just to kill time I rented a car and took my trout rod and drove out to have a look at the stream that Barbara's father had told me about. I found the pool, all right, and I crept up to the bank on my hands and knees and looked down just in time to see a V-shaped wake like a submarine heading upstream. I tell you, fellows, I never saw such a trout in my life.

"I waited several hours for Old One-Eye to quiet down and

go back to feeding again, and then I rigged my rod and put on a No. 14 Quill Gordon and dropped it in front of him. Nothing happened. I tried everything in the book, from a big Fanwing Coachman to a tiny Black Gnat, but he wouldn't pay any attention. They'd float over his nose, and he'd rise right behind them and take a natural insect instead. Oh, he was smart. Finally, in desperation, I put on a little nymph I'd tied myself. All the hairs were chewed off and it looked like a swatted mosquito, but I made a long cast upstream and the nymph drifted back down the current, right past Old One-Eye. Well, to make a long story short ..."

"Too late," Judge Parker grunted.

Colonel Cobb ignored him. "There was a swirl, I tightened, and he took off downstream. Did you ever hook into an Atlas missile? I chased that trout up and down, back and forth, and still I couldn't turn him. I waded out to my armpits, cutaway and striped pants and all, trying to lead him around into slack water. I'd have had him, too, except he made one last leap just as I lifted my rod, and the tip snapped off and he was gone. I crawled out of the stream with my broken rod and sat down on the bank to catch my breath, and I happened to glance at my watch. Four o'clock! The wedding was an hour ago.

"I drove back to town as fast as I could, wet clothes and all, and went right to the church. The door was locked, but I hammered on it, and the sexton came out and said he understood there'd been a wedding planned earlier that day but they'd called it off. I raced over to the country club where the reception was supposed to be, but nobody was around except a caterer who was carrying out some cases of unused champagne.

So I headed back to my hotel, and there was an envelope pinned to my door with the diamond engagement ring inside."

There was a lengthy pause. "What did you do?" Cousin Sid prompted.

"What did I do? Why, I did what any fisherman would do under the circumstances," Colonel Cobb replied. "I took the ring downtown to a jewelry store, and they gave me a very good price on it, enough to buy a new trout rod and also a reel and a dozen nymphs. As a matter of fact, it's the very same rod I'm using today." He opened the aluminum case and took out a slim section of split bamboo. "Best action I ever felt, light but plenty of backbone, and of course it means a lot to me because of its sentimental value."

He slid the rod section back gently into its case.

"Every time I fish with that rod I stop for a moment and think of Barb," he sighed, "and then I go right on fishing."

The Colonel twisted the metal cap onto the case, rose to his feet and started toward the door. "Guess that evening hatch ought to be ready about now," he said over his shoulder. "Sure sorry you fellows can't join me."

The door closed behind him, and the string of sleigh bells beside it tinkled softly, like the echo of far-off wedding chimes.

A Flavor All Their Own

Judge Parker opened the oven door a crack, allowing the savory aroma of roast fowl to waft through the kitchen. The other members of the Lower Forty peered hungrily over his shoulder at the array of birds in the broiler, each golden form capped with a strip of bacon. The Judge prodded them with a fork, nodded to himself with professional assurance and closed the door briskly. "They'll be ready in a few more minutes," he assured his guests, "and then you'll have a treat you'll never forget."

"First time I ever tasted sharptail," Cousin Sid admitted,

licking his lips in anticipation. "Are they anything like our ruffed grouse?"

"Oh no, sharptails have a flavor all their own," the Judge replied, pouring himself a well-earned tumblerful of Old Stump Blower. "That's why I flew them all the way back from Alberta . . ."

"Quite a long flight for a grouse," Doc Hall observed.

The Judge ignored him. ". . . so we could enjoy them here in private," he continued, "while the Ladies Club is having its annual supper at the parish house." He raised the tumbler to his lips and paused as a sudden thought struck him. He opened the oven door again and basted the birds with the contents of his glass, leaping back to avoid a billowing blue flame. "Helps bring out the flavor," he explained.

"Nobody will believe us," Colonel Cobb gloated, "when we tell them we were eating sharptail grouse in February."

Judge Parker frowned. "There's one favor I'd like to ask you," he said. "Don't ever mention to anybody what you had tonight." He hesitated. "Particularly my wife."

"What's so secret about it?" asked Uncle Perk.

"Well, it's a little involved," the Judge admitted, "but maybe I'd better tell you the whole story."

It all began last fall, Judge Parker informed his fellow members, when a telegram arrived from Frank Dufresne in Alberta. His friends Hugh Grey and Ed Zern were coming out from New York for a sharptail hunt in a few days, Frank's wire stated, and the Judge was invited to join them and make a foursome. This presented a slight domestic problem, inasmuch as the Judge had promised to drive his wife to Vermont that week to see the fall foliage, but he found a way to overcome her objections. "I'll bring back a mess of birds, dear," he offered, "and you can serve them at the annual supper of the Ladies Club. They'll create a real sensation."

The hunt was everything that Frank Dufresne had promised. For a week they worked the fields of wheat stubble, putting up covey after covey out of the windbreaks or around the deserted buildings of the old homestead farms. Usually a single sharp-tail would flush first, and the Judge would empty both barrels and then fumble for more shells as half-a-dozen additional birds got up in front of him and sailed away unscathed. But at last he got the knack of centering on them, and each of the party brought his limit to Lethbridge to be frozen and packed for carrying home.

"They'll make nice presents for your friends," Frank Dufresne suggested.

"You don't catch us giving these birds away," Hugh Grey replied as he carried his package out to the waiting plane. "We're saving them for ourselves. Isn't that right, Judge?"

Judge Parker sighed unhappily. The more he thought of the rash offer he had made to his wife, the more he regretted it. After all, he reflected, these sharptails were worth their weight in gold when you added up the cost of transportation plus lodging and license and shells, and it was nothing short of criminal to waste them all on a church supper. Not only that, but the members of the Ladies Club would never appreciate anything as exotic as sharptail grouse, he brooded. Why, they probably couldn't tell the difference between them and any other bird.

"That's when I had my inspiration," Judge Parker confided to the Lower Forty. "The very next morning I went down to the meat market and bought a dozen guinea hens, and after they were cleaned and plucked you wouldn't know them from sharptail. Just to make it more convincing, though, I got an ice pick and poked them full of little holes, and shoved in some pieces of shot, No. 4's and 2's and even a few Lubaloy-plated BB's from my reloading kit, so the gals would be sure to find them. Then I wrapped them in a package just like the one from Lethbridge and put it right on top of the freezer, and I hid the real sharptails down in the bottom of the box under some frozen peas."

"Did it work?" asked Cousin Sid.

"Like a charm," the Judge chuckled. "My wife never suspected a thing." He opened the oven door, took out the trayful of bronzed birds, and set one on each plate with a flourish. "Just sink your fangs into those," he urged, "and tell me if you ever tasted anything like them in your life."

The members cut into their birds and munched on the tender flesh with relish. Doc Hall winced and removed a piece of shot from his mouth. He studied it thoughtfully.

"Yes, sir, there's something distinctive about the flavor of sharptail," the Judge insisted, rolling a morsel on his tongue with the appreciation of a true epicure. "Probably comes from feeding on that Alberta wheat. You can recognize it every time."

"By the way," Doc inquired, "what size shot were you using out there?"

"Oh, 7½'s," Judge Parker answered casually. "The birds

get up pretty far away, so you need to . . ." His voice trailed and a shadow of doubt crossed his face. "Why do you ask?"

Doc Hall dropped the shot onto his plate with a loud clink. "This looks to me like a 4, or even a 2."

"Must have been a shell I borrowed from Hugh Grey or Ed Zern," the Judge faltered, staring at the pellet with growing misgiving.

Colonel Cobb put on his glasses and examined his own bird with interest. "Certainly remarkable how these shot holes are distributed," he commented. "Each about an inch apart."

"That gun of mine throws a very even pattern," Judge Parker said, but his voice had a hollow sound.

"Thing I can't understand," Uncle Perk murmured, inspecting a handful of shot, "is how they're all so nice an' round an' shiny. Us'ally the lead gets stove up when it hits a bird."

The front door slammed and Patience Parker entered the kitchen. "Enjoying your sharptails, dear?" she asked, patting the Judge's cheek affectionately.

Judge Parker shook his head in bewilderment. "But—these birds were meant for you."

"I know, dear, you were sweet to offer them." His wife smiled. "But I decided it wasn't fair to take them, after you'd gone to all that trouble to shoot them. So I found another package of birds down at the bottom of the freezer, and that's what I served at the supper instead." She gazed curiously at the half-finished carcasses on the plates. "Tell me, what do sharptails taste like?"

"Oh, they've got a flavor all their own," Doc Hall said with a sly glance at the Judge. "Almost like guinea hen."

"Some folks couldn't tell the difference," Uncle Perk agreed.

Judge Parker bit down on a hard object with one of his four remaining good teeth and uttered a yelp of pain. He removed a Lubaloy-plated BB shot and gazed at it malevolently.

"There's one favor I'd like to ask you," his wife added. "Don't ever mention to the other girls what I did. They all think they were eating sharptails tonight."

"We'll keep it a secret," Colonel Cobb assured her. "Won't we, Judge?"

Judge Parker held his aching jaw and nodded in silence.

Trick or Treat

Colonel Cobb slammed the front door of Uncle Perk's store so hard that the string of sleigh bells jangled wildly, and confronted the other members of the Lower Forty Shooting, Angling and Inside Straight Club. "Look at this order I just received at the printshop," he said dramatically, holding up a sheet of paper on which was lettered: NO HUNTING OR FISHING. TRESPASSERS WILL BE PROSECUTED. (SIGNED) B.D. BANKS. He flung it on the counter indignantly. "He wants a hundred copies to post his entire land."

"Who's B.D. Banks?" asked Cousin Sid.

72

"He's a retired stockbroker from the city who's decided to locate here in Hardscrabble," Colonel Cobb explained. "I hear he's a widower with more money than he knows what to do with . . ."

"I'd be hoppy to fur-r-rnish him with a wee suggestion," Mr. MacNab murmured.

". . . and he's just bought the old Nellie Goss place on Goss Hill." The Colonel paused to give added emphasis to his words. "He's going to turn it into a private sanctuary."

His fellow members stared at one another incredulously. For years Goss Hill had been one of their favorite hunting covers. Grouse were always abundant in the stands of pine and thorn apples, the birches on the hillside were loaded with flight woodcock each fall, and at the base of the hill Mink Brook wound through the meadow in a series of slow, deep runs where trout rose hungrily to flies.

"Why would he want to keep sportsmen out?" Cousin Sid mourned. "They help to control predators; they feed the wild-life in winter; they restock the stream . . ."

Judge Parker banged his fist on Uncle Perk's desk. "He can't get away with it. We'll run him out of town."

The Colonel shook his head. "Not a chance. They say he's fallen in love with the Goss place. It would take a load of dynamite to blast him off."

The sleigh bells jangled and two urchins stuck their heads in the door. They were dressed in ragamuffin clothes and their faces were blackened. "Trick or treat, Uncle Perk," they shrilled, "or else we'll soap your front window!"

"Durn Halloween," Uncle Perk grumbled, scooping a handful of gumdrops from his showcase and tossing them to the children. He scowled as they disappeared. "Feller ain't safe tonight 'less he gives 'em whatever they want."

"Trick or treat," Judge Parker echoed thoughtfully. His eyes suddenly lighted. "Gentlemen, I've got an idea. Start blacking your faces," he ordered. "Uncle Perk, we'll need to borrow a few sticks of dynamite and some other little items." He rubbed his hands in anticipation. "This is going to be a Halloween to remember. . . ."

B.D. Banks, seated in the living room of his new home on Goss Hill, looked up in surprise as heavy steps sounded on his front porch. He opened the door and blinked at a group of disheveled figures, their coats inside out and their faces smeared with burnt cork. Judge Parker held a roll of blasting wire and a magneto, and several sticks of dynamite protruded from his hip pocket. Uncle Perk toted a power saw; Cousin Sid brandished a pair of wire cutters; Doc Hall had a large can of yellow paint. Colonel Cobb was lugging a fifty-pound sack of calcium chloride. Mr. MacNab stood in the rear, armed with a claw hammer. B.D. Banks extended his hand in cordial greeting.

"Well now, this is a pleasant surprise," he beamed. "I've been hoping some of the neighbors would drop by and get acquainted."

"We weren't exactly planning a social call," Judge Parker said, slightly taken aback.

"But you're the first company I've had since I moved here," B.D. Banks insisted hospitably. "You'll have to come in and let me mix you some highballs to celebrate the occasion. They'll probably taste good after working in the woods all day," he added, noting the collection of tools in their hands. "Maybe you'd like to wash some of that grime off your faces. . . ."

The Judge tried to keep control of things. "Just a moment, Mr. Banks," he said sternly, pausing in the doorway. "I understand you're planning to post all this land."

"Yes, that was a suggestion that Deacon Godfrey made," B.D. Banks nodded. The group raised their eyebrows and exchanged significant glances. "Do you know the Deacon?" he asked.

"We know him all too well," Doc Hall muttered darkly.

"He said I ought to establish a sanctuary and preserve the wildlife so I could study it. You see, I've always lived in the city, and I've never had a chance to learn about nature."

"Well, the first thing to learn," the Judge informed him, "is that stopping all hunting and fishing doesn't preserve the wildlife. The deer overbrowse and die of starvation in the winter, and your place will be overrun with wildcats and foxes, because there are no sportsmen to help keep them down. The best plan is to establish a game-management area, with controlled shooting to crop the surplus, and start a program of restocking and planting food patches and stream improvement."

"Well, I certainly do appreciate your advice," B.D. Banks said gratefully. "It sounds like a much better plan than the Deacon's. As a matter of fact," he suggested, "maybe you chaps would be willing to handle the program for me, and teach me about hunting and fishing. It's something I've always dreamed of doing when I retired." He apologized: "But here I'm talking and keeping you waiting for those highballs. Make yourselves comfortable, and I'll be back in a jiffy."

The members of the Lower Forty seated themselves in the living room and gazed at each other sheepishly. "Seems like a real nice fellow," Doc Hall whispered.

"I think it might be nice if we invited him to join the Lower Forty," Cousin Sid recommended.

"I move his election," said Colonel Cobb. "It's time we had a treasurer who pays his own dues."

Mr. MacNab started to bristle, but relaxed as their host returned with a tray of drinks. "By the way, B.D.," Judge Parker inquired, "how long have you known this Deacon Godfrey?"

"Oh, he came up and introduced himself when he heard I was looking for property. Claimed he was a distant cousin of Nellie Goss, and he wanted to be the first to show me her land. I've signed an agreement to pay him fifteen percent finder's commission."

The Judge choked on his drink. "Why, that conniving old skinflint," he spluttered. "I bet he's charging old Nellie Goss a commission, too."

"That's right," B.D. Banks nodded. "Fifteen percent. He said it was a local custom."

Judge Parker set his glass on the table and rose. "Gentlemen, Halloween isn't over yet. We've got another call to make". . . .

Deacon Godfrey winced as his front door shook under a heavy thudding of fists. He flung it open and glowered at the members of the Lower Forty. His eyes moved from their blackened faces to the array of lethal items they were carrying. "Trick or treat," Judge Parker smiled grimly.

"Git off this property," the Deacon ordered, backing a few steps.

"Now Deacon," the Judge reminded him, tapping the dynamite sticks in his hip pocket, "you wouldn't want that nice hen house of yours lifted clear across the barn."

"I imagine these wire cutters would do quite a job on the fence around your sheep pasture," Cousin Sid remarked.

"This here power saw works mighty fast on old wood," Uncle Perk pointed out, gazing at the porch pillars speculatively.

"Sure would feel sorry if this bag of calcium chloride slipped out of my hand," Colonel Cobb sighed, "and got down inside your well."

"Wh-what do you want?" Deacon Godfrey faltered.

"Just those two agreements you signed with B.D. Banks and Nellie Goss," Judge Parker replied, "or else we'll start to work."

"I'll have the law onto ye," the Deacon gasped. "I'll bring charges of unlawful entry and . . ."

"My friend," the Judge said serenely, "at this very moment I happen to be fifty miles from here at a magistrates' conference in the state capitol, as fifteen reputable fellow judges are prepared to swear."

"I've got a roomful of surgeons and nurses and interns," Doc Hall added, "who will testify that right now I'm at the hospital, busily engaged in removing a hot appendix."

"Anybody in town'll tell ye," said Uncle Perk, "that I ain't left my store all evenin'."

The Deacon snarled, fumbled in his jacket, and handed the

agreements to Judge Parker in sullen silence. The Judge tore them into little pieces and beckoned to the other members. "Well, let's all get back to B.D.'s and notify him of his election to the club." He paused. "Hey, Mac, where are you?"

"R-r-right here," called Mr. MacNab, emerging from the shadows with his claw hammer. He followed them to the car, a broad smile on his face.

"Wotinell are you grinning about?" the Judge asked curiously.

"Well, I thought it might be nice if the Deacon had some fun on Halloween," Mr. MacNab explained, "so I pr-r-ried out a few nails under that Chic Sale of his behind the bar-r-r-n." He chuckled to himself. "Wish we could stay ar-r-round long enough to see him tip over his own oothoose."

The Quick and the Dead

A light December snow was falling, and Uncle Perk crammed another chunk of dry apple wood into the potbellied stove and replaced the lid in heavy silence. There were no smiles on the faces of the other members of the Lower Forty huddled around its warming glow; the death of Effie Libbey's eldest boy was weighing on all their minds.

Two days earlier his frozen body had been found at the bottom of the Libbey swamp, drilled through the chest by a bullet from a deer rifle. Evidently the hunter had fired at something in the bushes and had not stayed to investigate whether his shot had

79

connected, and young Libbey could not summon help. He had crawled about a hundred yards in the snow, and there were signs that he had tried to build a fire during the night before numbness set in.

"He was bringin' home a Christmas tree," Uncle Perk recalled bitterly, "and somebody must of seen a patch of white snow an' a branch movin'."

"Same thing happened down at Cushin's Corners last week," Judge Parker nodded. "Two partners hunting together, one of them shoots a rabbit and waves it in the air, the other one hears the shot and sees a flash of white . . ." The Judge spread his hands.

"Fellow who did it was one of the best hunters around," Cousin Sid added. "Now he never wants to hunt again." He shook his head. "What's the answer to it all?"

"Pairhaps it would help if I ran an ad in Colonel Cobb's newspaper," Mr. MacNab suggested grimly, "offering free bur-r-rial sairvice and a tombstone for the first legal r-r-resident of Hardscrabble County who is killed by a deer hunter each fall." His voice was hard. "Might shock people into thinking twice before they point a r-r-rifle at something they canna see."

"Mebbe the only answer," Uncle Perk grunted, "is for everybody to stay indoors till deer season's over. . . ."

"Hey, can I innerup' your gabfest?" a voice inquired from the front of the store. "I need some more .30–30's."

Uncle Perk peered over his spectacles at the impatient customer. A nonresident license was pinned to his red-checkered shirt, his high-laced boots were gleaming new, and a shiny deer rifle was hooked over a forearm. Uncle Perk reached for a box of ammunition on a high shelf. "Any luck this mornin'?" he inquired over his shoulder.

"Had three shots," the stranger reported proudly. "One sight and two sound."

Uncle Perk glowered as he set the box on the counter. "Where was you huntin'?"

"Listen, Pop, you don't think I'm gonna give away my pet deer cover so you can go there?"

"I don't figger to go there, mister," Uncle Perk said thinly. "I figger to stay away." He pocketed the customer's money and turned his back.

The stranger grinned. "On'y kidding, Pop. I been working one side of Moose Mountain this morning, and my brother and some local guide we hired, name of Finney, they're driving the other side. Heard a lot of shooting and hollering right after we separated," he added, "so I guess they got into something. . . ."

The string of sleigh bells inside the front door jangled and Colonel Cobb entered the store. He slumped wearily into a chair beside the stove and reached for a cigarette. "I'm beat," he sighed. "Been working all morning on another shooting."

"Same old story?" Judge Parker asked.

Colonel Cobb nodded. "That's the trouble with being a country editor," he sighed. "It's the same story year after year. I could write it in my sleep." He passed a tired hand across his eyes. "There's always the waiting room of the hospital, and the man who pulled the trigger is sitting in one corner with his head in his hands. The conservation officers have taken his knife and his rifle away, just to be on the safe side, and he's had a shot in the arm, and now he is mercifully numb. He doesn't want to smoke or have a cup of coffee or talk. He just sits there."

The others nodded in understanding. The customer had halted on his way to the door and was listening curiously.

"And a woman is sitting across the waiting room," the Colonel went on, almost as though he were talking to himself. "She's only been a widow for fifteen minutes, and she is in shock. The tears just won't come. She stares straight ahead, and an older woman beside her pats her clumsily on the shoulder and keeps saying, 'There, there, there,' because she's in shock, too. It was her son.

"And the state trooper says to me, 'Look, will you get your camera out of the car, Cobbie, we want to get a good shot of the portal of entry before the doc goes in after the bullet.' So I get my camera, and I go into the emergency operating room and it's always the same in there, too. The pile of hunting clothes thrown into a corner, the boots and the socks and the pants and the red shirt that wasn't quite red enough, and the figure on the table under a sheet, and Doc Hall pulls back the sheet and it's Asa Finney, the guide. . . ."

Colonel Cobb took a long drag on his cigarette. The stranger in the checkered shirt had sagged against the counter behind him. His face suddenly looked sick.

"So I aim my camera at the hole in the skull, and adjust the range finder, and clip the dark slide onto the back of the camera, and I take a deep breath and let it half out and squeeze, just like a rifle; and then I put in the dark slide, and reverse the plateholder, and open up half a stop to vary the exposure and I shoot again.

"And meantime Doc Hall is telling me, 'We got him onto the table and were starting a transfusion when he began to fade. The boys had tried hard, but it took too long getting him down off Moose Mountain and he lost too much blood.' Doc's voice doesn't sound very steady, because no matter how many times you see these things, it's never easy, and I case my camera and Doc goes back to probing for the slug.

"And I step out into the waiting room again," Colonel Cobb concluded, grinding out his cigarette, "and it's the same as it was, only the widow has begun to cry. And the man who pulled the trigger looks up at me questioning, and I shake my head no and he moans, 'My God, I didn't mean to. I heard him blow his nose and I saw his white handkerchief and I thought . . .' They always say the same thing, and what can you say to them? He wasn't a killer, just somebody from the city who came up here to go deer hunting and saw a flash of something white."

The stranger was working hard to swallow. Abruptly he clapped a hand over his mouth and ran out the door, and they could hear the sound of retching in the gutter.

"Rough," Cousin Sid murmured.

"Sure it's rough," Judge Parker said. "It's always rough, from the time the hammer drops and the smell of death goes through the woods, to the time years later when the oldest child has finished school and can go to work now to help the widow support the rest of the family." He shrugged. "I'd rather take a licking than do what I have to do tomorrow." The Judge climbed slowly to his feet.

"What are you going to do to him tomorrow?" Cousin Sid asked.

"That's not a fair question. I'm not in the habit of prejudging cases," Judge Parker replied. "Let's put it this way. No man ever loaded up a rifle and went deer hunting with the idea he might kill another hunter before sundown. He does it, though, and then he cries and maybe tries suicide and goes through a little hell all his own. But you can't substitute his self-punishment for public punishment." The Judge paused in the door. "If you give him sympathy instead of a sentence, God alone knows where this man-killing would stop."

The Judge walked down the store steps and placed a gentle hand on the shoulder of the stranger bent over in the gutter. "Let's go find your brother," he said quietly.

The man straightened, and they walked down the street together. Uncle Perk closed the door and gazed through the glass pane at the fresh blanket of white on the ground.

"Stopped snowin'," he observed to the others. "Ought to be good trackin' this afternoon. They'll all be goin' out in the woods." He tossed another apple log into the stove. "Wonder if they'll all be comin' back."

Women Are All Alike

Cousin Sid put his problem up to the other members of the Lower Forty Shooting, Angling and Inside Straight Club. "I hate to ask this favor," he apologized, "when we're all planning to go bass fishing in Beaver Lake this afternoon, but I wonder if you'd mind getting your shotguns and rifles and dropping over to my house for a few minutes. It's my wife," he explained.

"Ye plannin' to shoot yer wife?" asked Uncle Perk in surprise.

"Oh no, not that," said Cousin Sid hastily. "There's a colony of red squirrels that she wants me to get rid of."

85

"Now, what does she have against a few wee squair-r-rels?" Mr. MacNab protested.

"They eat all the sunflower seeds out of her bird-feeding station," Cousin Sid replied, "and raid the robins' nests and steal their eggs, and drive all the gray squirrels away, and last night when she went up to the attic she found a family of seven young ones in a bundle of my long woolen underwear. She says I've got to do something about them," he sighed, "before I go fishing."

"Why don't you get some traps?" Doc Hall suggested.

Cousin Sid shook his head. "Sally couldn't bear to see them suffer."

"Women are all alike," Colonel Cobb snorted. "Sometimes I'm glad I'm still a bachelor."

"Well, I move we all give Sid a hand," Judge Parker said, sliding his rump off Uncle Perk's counter. "Let's meet at his house in an hour and clean the varmints out." He shrugged. "Besides, the fishing isn't much good this time of day anyway."

An hour later the members of the Lower Forty, armed with appropriate weapons, followed Cousin Sid stealthily to the rear of his house. It was a rambling gingerbread structure with cupolas and gables and a slanting slate roof surmounted by a central chimney with an elaborate tile chimney pot. Several acrobatic squirrels were shinnying up and down the lightning rods, chinning themselves on the rotary TV antenna and performing aerial somersaults in the branches of the overhanging elm. Judge Parker flung a hand aloft for caution, and the jungle patrol halted.

"The best plan is to use a precision weapon," he whispered,

"with minimum load to cause the least possible damage." He produced a Model 52 Winchester Sporter fitted with a 2½X Lyman scope that had a fine cross-hair reticle. "I'll slip in a BB cap," he told Cousin Sid, "which is much lower in power than a short."

The Judge waited until one of the squirrels paused on the ridgepole, then took a solid bead and squeezed off. There was a tiny crack, like the snap of a buggy whip, and the ornate porcelain ball on one of the lightning rods exploded into a thousand pieces. Judge Parker stared dumfounded at his rifle, and his eyes moved accusingly to his wife's nephew standing beside him.

"Guess I forgot to tell you, Judge," Dexter Smeed admitted. "I was target shooting with your rifle yesterday, and I put about a dozen clicks in the scope to get the right windage. Probably I should have mentioned it."

All the squirrels had scampered to safety but one, which perched on top of the rotary antenna, preening its whiskers. Colonel Cobb stepped forward with his 10-bore magnum. "I'll use No. 10 shot and a light load of powder," he assured Cousin Sid, taking a shell from his pocket. "Can't hurt anything with that low velocity."

Cousin Sid held his breath as the Colonel touched off his weapon with a loud *ka*-POW! The rotary antenna snapped clean off and came tumbling down the roof, landing with a crash in the nasturtium bed. Cousin Sid stared mutely at the twisted wreckage. "Well, that's one on me, all right," Colonel Cobb chuckled. "I must have inserted an experimental super-magnum slug load by mistake."

" 'Tain't sportin' to use a scattergun on a squir'l, anyhow," Uncle Perk objected, grasping his .22 Hornet, which had a heavy barrel fitted onto a Sharps Borchardt action and a 10X Unertl scope and ultra-fine crosshairs. "Thing is to bark it the way the oldtimers used to."

"Bark?" Cousin Sid echoed faintly.

"That's right," Uncle Perk nodded. "Shoot under the critter and put some splinters into its belly. Kill it with the shock." He followed the racing squirrel across the ridgepole and fired just as it leapt toward an elm branch. The bullet plowed a path through the slate, and several shattered sections detached themselves and rattled down the roof and dropped into the yard. Cousin Sid sat down heavily on the back steps and emitted a low moan.

"The safest way to dispotch a var-r-rmint," Mr. MacNab stated, stepping up to the firing line, "is with an old-foshioned bow and arr-r-row. My grandfeyther-r-r always used it when he was poaching back in the old countr-r-ry."

He drew from his quiver a hunting arrow fitted with an empty .30-20 cartridge for a head, and struck his best Robin Hood pose. The squirrel was swinging from the elm branch, and Mr. MacNab pulled back his bowstring and released it with a loud twang. The arrow sailed across the ridgepole and disappeared, followed an instant later by a distant tinkle of glass. The members peered around the corner at a jagged hole in the picture window of the house next door. Cousin Sid buried his face in his hands.

"Dinna worry, Sidney," Mr. MacNab consoled him. "I hoppen to know that the owne-r-r-r has a verra bad heart; he'll doubtless drop dead when he sees the damage, and ye willna have to pay a bawbee." Cousin Sid shook his head and groaned. "What's mor-r-re," Mr. MacNab promised him, "if the executo-r-r-r of the estate pr-r-resents a bill, I'll mark up the casket twenty per cent to cove-r-r-r the expenses."

Doc Hall uncased a .375 H. & H. Model 70, fitted with a 4X Bausch & Lomb scope, and inserted a solid bullet meant for elephant. "If you fellows are through fooling around," he jeered, "I'll dispatch that squirrel once and for all." He scanned the rooftop. "Anybody see where he went?"

"There he is," Dexter shouted. "Right on top of the chimney."

Doc nodded, braced himself against the side of the garage and started to squeeze just as the squirrel ducked behind the chimney pot. Like a veteran deer hunter, Doc swung with him and touched off, and the chimney pot disintegrated in a cloud splintered tile. The squirrel stuck out its head from the other side, and Doc instinctively flipped the bolt and fired again. A section of the chimney crumbled, and the loose bricks cascaded down the roof in gathering crescendo, drumming loudly over the slate and landing with a final deafening crash on the ornamental crystal globe in the rock garden below. A moment later there was a soft thud at their feet, and Doc stooped over and lifted the dead squirrel by his tail. "How did you like that shot?" he demanded triumphantly.

"You missed him clean," Judge Parker muttered enviously. "It was the fall that killed him."

A car honked in the driveway, and Cousin Sid lifted his head in alarm as his station wagon rolled to a halt. His wife emerged from the car, her arms full of bundles, and stared at the littered yard. "Sidney, what happened?" she gasped.

"We just got rid of a squirrel, dear," Cousin Sid said weakly.

Sally stared at the limp object in Doc's hand and her lower lip quivered. "Is—is it dead?" she asked in a wavering voice.

"Dead as a her-r-ring," Mr. MacNab announced proudly. "It willna bother ye again."

Sally's eyes brimmed with tears. "Oh, the poor little thing." She whirled on the circle of members. "You ought to be ashamed of yourselves," she cried, "shooting a defenseless creature like that. I'll never speak to any of you again."

She burst into hysterical sobs, raced for the house and slammed the back door.

Cousin Sid ran up the steps after her as the key turned in the lock. He tried the knob in vain. "Please, Sally," he begged, "listen to me, dear. . . ."

Judge Parker glanced uneasily at his watch. "It's getting late," he said. "We better get started for Beaver Lake."

"You go ahead without me," Cousin Sid called over his shoulder. "I've got to explain to Sally."

The rest of the members piled into Mr. MacNab's hearse. "As I was saying," Colonel Cobb repeated, "women are all alike." He glanced back through the rear window at Cousin Sid, still banging his fists forlornly on the locked door of his house. "The only difference is that some women are more alike than others."

The Children's Derby

Everyone nodded in approval as Owl Eyes Osborn made his appeal to the Lower Forty Shooting, Angling and Inside Straight Club. "As you know, the Conservation Department is trying to encourage sportsmanship in the younger generation," he explained to the members gathered around the stove in Uncle Perk's store. "So we've decided to set aside a section of stream on opening day tomorrow, and hold a fishing derby for the school children. We're asking every sportsman in town to contribute a dollar apiece to pay for the awards."

"Don't the kids have school tomorrow?" asked Colonel Cobb as he handed Owl Eyes his donation.

"I've taken care of that," Cousin Sid replied, tossing a dollar into the kitty. "As school principal, I'm excusing them all from morning classes." He added ruefully, "They'd only cut school anyway."

"Sounds like a fine idea to me," Judge Parker stated. "Teach the young reptiles to do something useful, like fishing."

"Aye, it's a wor-r-rthy cause," Mr. MacNab agreed, reaching for his wallet. "When I was a wee bairn I won a dollar in a contest once, and I've ne'er forgot it." He took out a crumpled oversize bill and gazed at it thoughtfully. "In fact, I believe this is the verra same dollar."

Doc Hall completed the collection and winked at the others as Owl Eyes departed. "Personally, I'd be in favor of a prize of our own on opening day," he observed with a meaningful glance at Uncle Perk. "Might give some incentive to the Lower Forty."

"Okay, okay," Uncle Perk grumbled, opening the bottom drawer of his desk. "Here's a jug of Old Stump Blower for the biggest fish." He glowered over his spectacles. "But it's got to be took on a fly."

"You might as well present me with that prize right now," Doc said with a superior smile. "I've got an old walloper all staked out, and the rest of you don't stand a chance." He chuckled to himself as he sauntered toward the door. "See you on Mink Brook tomorrow."

Next morning Doc Hall was still chuckling as he strolled across the Widow Libbey's pasture toward the brook. A week ago he had spotted a fine two-pound squaretail lying under a sunken log at the lower end of his favorite pool. Day after day, unknown to the others, he had studied its feeding habits and planned his strategy. Now all he had to do was float a Gray Ghost downstream, give the least little flick to his rod as the fly drifted past the log, and he would be the prize winner. His grin broadened as he thought of Judge Parker's crestfallen expression. It suddenly faded. From the direction of the stream came a series of squeals and high-pitched laughter, punctuated by the unmistakable voice of Owl Eyes Osborn shouting orders.

Doc hurried across the meadow and halted aghast. Mink Brook was filled with youngsters in hip boots, splashing up and down the stream and flailing the water with metal rods and homemade poles, while their parents shouted encouragement from the bank. The other members of the Lower Forty were grouped glumly beside a poster tacked on a hemlock tree: CHILDREN'S DERBY. THIS SECTION OF STREAM IS CLOSED TO ALL FISHERMEN OVER TWELVE YEARS OLD.

"Owl Eyes can't do that to us," Doc gasped. "We've fished this private stretch every opening day for years."

"The Widow Libbey gave permission," Judge Parker sighed, "as her contribution to the derby." He frowned at a freckled youngster in the center of the stream, waving his pole awkwardly in the air and slamming a gob of worms into the water. "Not so hard, sonny," the Judge advised. "You'll scare every fish away. Just toss it out nice and easy."

Colonel Cobb was watching a small boy fumbling with his reel as he tried to let out line. "You're winding it in, Junior," he pointed out. "Turn the handle the other way."

"Luik at that little tot there with a fish on," Mr. MacNab

exclaimed, pointing downstream at a red-haired youth with his rod bent almost double. "Dinna hor-r-rse it, lad," he called, running down the bank toward him. "Ca' canny, or ye'll lose it surely."

Uncle Perk stroked his stubbled chin thoughtfully. "Tell you what I'll do," he suggested. "Seein' as how we can't fish ourselves, I'll give the prize to the member o' the club who helps a kid get the biggest one."

The members scattered eagerly up and down the stream, but they were not gone long. Uncle Perk had barely settled himself at the base of the hemlock when Mr. MacNab reappeared, followed by the red-haired youth holding his rod high in the air. "Dinna tug, lad," Mr. MacNab pleaded. "Keep a slack line."

"What happened?" Uncle Perk asked.

"He huiked me right in the ear," Mr. MacNab groaned as he passed, "and he willna let me cut his feyther's line, so we've got to go back to town togither while I have the bar-r-rb removed." He started up the bank. "Lower-r-r yere r-r-rod a bit," he called over his shoulder to his captor, "and mind the br-r-ronches."

A resounding splash echoed around the bend, and a moment later Colonel Cobb strode toward Uncle Perk, water cascading down his clothes and his boots squishing soggily. "Lost my balance while I was showing Junior how to net a trout," he explained grumpily, "and now he blames me for losing his fish."

Uncle Perk leapt to his feet, startled, as a series of terrified screams shook the air. Cousin Sid galloped into sight, hotly pursued by an indignant mother who held an hysterical little girl by the hand. "You ought to be ashamed of yourself, baiting a hook right in front of a poor defenseless child," she shouted, switching Cousin Sid with a cane pole as he scrambled up the bank. "Elsie's scared to death of worms."

At the head of the long run, Judge Parker was still coaching his freckled protégé, gazing covertly now and then at Doc Hall, who watched from the opposite shore. "Let's try a little weight on your line, sonny," the Judge suggested, handing the youngster a split shot. "Now cast it as far out in the current as you can, and wait for the bait to settle before you pull it in. That's right. Now a couple of tugs to make it bounce along the bottom." Suddenly the line tightened, the reel began to sing and the Judge gave a triumphant glance across the stream at Doc. "Start reeling in, son," he coached as the trout halted its run. "No, not too fast. Just keep it coming—that's right. Lead it around into the slack water. Get your net under it. Now *lift!*"

Judge Parker beamed at Doc as the freckled youth held up the trout wriggling in his net. "Ought to go a pound at least," he taunted his rival on the opposite bank. "Guess you don't stand a chance, Doc."

Doc Hall moved disconsolately down the bank toward his favorite pool. A towheaded boy of ten was standing in the water, almost to the tops of his rubber boots, chucking a limp worm into the current. Doc's eye traveled back upstream to Judge Parker, who was proudly displaying his protégé's catch to Owl Eyes, and his jaw set in grim resolve. "Let me have your line a minute, Bud," he called to the boy. "I've got a different kind of lure for you to try."

Doc quickly removed the hook and replaced it with a Gray Ghost. He paused, peering at the Judge to make sure he was not observed, then fumbled for a moment with the fly. He tossed it into the water beside the boy.

"Do exactly what I tell you," he said in a low voice. "Let the current carry it downstream and keep paying out your line." He watched the fly drift nearer and nearer the sunken log. "Now then," he instructed, "give your rod the least little flick ..."

The water beside the log exploded and the back of a huge squaretail showed for a moment as the fish swirled and sounded. Judge Parker hurried down the bank, attracted by the commotion, and stared crestfallen as Doc's pupil fought the big trout. At last the boy led it around in front of him, kicked it into the bank with his rubber boot, and sprawled on it as it flapped across the gravel. Doc quieted the fish with a swift blow and lifted it by its gills.

"Better than two pounds," he informed the Judge, handing the trout to its happy owner. "And what's more, it was taken on a fly!"

A delicate cough sounded behind him. "Naow, I dunno if I'd go so far's to say that, Doc," Uncle Perk murmured in his ear. "I happened to be standin' in them bushes when you tied on your fly, and I couldn't help but see that live grasshopper you sneaked onto the hook."

Doc Hall's face fell. "You won't ever mention it, will you?" he begged as the boy carried his trophy proudly to Owl Eyes

Osborn. "After all, we want to encourage sportsmanship in the younger generation."

"Oh, I won't say nawthin'," Uncle Perk agreed, "exceptin', under the circumstances, I think this prize jug of Old Stump Blower belongs to the whole club."

Strictly for the Birds

"The nicest thing about the Lower Forty Shooting, Angling and Inside Straight Club," boasted Judge Parker, as he led the way on snowshoes across the white wasteland, "is the self-sacrifice and generosity of its members. They think nothing of hiking ten miles in sub-zero weather to scatter winter feed for the birds."

"I don't think so much of it myself," admitted Colonel Cobb, because the straps of his snowshoes were beginning to saw across his insteps.

"How much further do we have to go?" asked Cousin Sid,

bringing up the tail of the procession. "This bag of corn weighs a ton. Why can't birds eat something lighter, like hay?"

"It's only another mile or so," Judge Parker reassured him. "I thought we might set up our feeding station in front of one of those summer cottages on the shore of the lake. There's a sort of sheltered place where we can spread out the feed.

"Why do we have to hang up the suet?" Dexter Smeed asked.

"To get the wrinkles out," Colonel Cobb said sourly.

Doc Hall set down the sack of apples he was carrying, and mopped his forehead. "Why don't we spread the feed right here and let the birds come get it?" he suggested. "After all, they don't have to walk."

Judge Parker glared at him. "Why don't you quit crabbing?" he asked. "Think of this winter wonderland that we're enjoying. Think of the cool crisp air. Think of the silence."

"Think of that jug of Old Stump Blower back in Uncle Perk's store," Doc Hall sighed, as the procession started moving again. The branches of the overhanging trees were laden with fresh-fallen snow, which sifted down their necks as they walked beneath. The air was filled with flying crystals. "By the way, Judge, do you have any idea where we are?"

"Of course I know where we are," said Judge Parker indignantly. "I come from a long line of outdoorsmen. My grandfather used to run a trap line in Maine until he made enough money to get the hell out and move to Florida instead. A good woodsman can read the signs in the snow just like the pages of a book."

"Then what are these tracks right here, for instance?" asked Dexter Smeed.

"That's a rabbit," the Judge announced confidently. "See the two short prints of his front legs and the two larger prints of his hind legs? That tells you the direction he's running." He pointed to a series of pawprints in the snow. "That's a fox. Probably chasing the rabbit."

"You've got it backward," Doc Hall scoffed. "The hind legs of a rabbit are always ahead of the front legs. He's going the other way."

"Probably the rabbit was chasing the fox," suggested Colonel Cobb.

"Here's a snake track," said Dexter excitedly. "See this long mark in the trail right where we've been walking?"

"That's not a snake," Doc Hall shrugged. "That's the Judge's suspenders dragging." He shook his head. "I'll bet we're lost."

"A good woodsman is never lost," Judge Parker insisted. He paused beside a plank nailed to a tree, and rubbed the snow from it with his sleeve.

It read: BIDE-A-WEE COTTAGES, ¼ MILE.

"See what I mean?" Judge Parker said triumphantly. "All you have to do is read the signs."

The party unloaded their packsacks in relief as they reached the cabin, and Judge Parker set about busily trampling down the snow. While he scattered the corn, the rest of the members spiked apples onto broken twigs and hung bits of suit from the branches of the trees. They completed their labors and paused expectantly. Not a bird note could be heard.

"What do we have to do now?" asked Colonel Cobb. "Climb a tree and wake up the little so-and-sos and tell 'em dinner's ready?"

"We'd better get started back," Judge Parker advised. "The sun's getting low, and we want to be out of the woods before dark. I know a shortcut around the lake that will save us several miles."

The shadows grew longer and longer as they trudged through the snow, following the Judge. The wind was sharper as the sun dipped below the horizon, and their cheekbones began to ache with the cold. Birch twigs whipped their faces, icicles formed on their noses, and their eyes watered. The Judge led the way across a frozen swamp, and they climbed a ridge and slithered down the other side, then halted in a tangle of alders at the edge of a lake.

Judge Parker scratched his head. "That's funny," he muttered. "I never knew there was *another* lake back here."

Dexter Smeed called excitedly. "What are these tracks?"

"That's a bear," Judge Parker informed them, after a nervous glance. "He's a big one, too." The members drew a little closer together. "Here's three or four more bears walking right behind him."

Doc Hall picked up something from the snow. "I didn't know that bears smoked cigarettes," he commented thinly.

They followed the tracks in silence to Bide-a-Wee Cottage, and pushed open the front door. Someone lit a kerosene lamp, and they peered glumly around the bleak cabin. Cousin Sid found some firewood and started a blaze in the iron stove. He scanned the cupboard, but the shelves were bare. "If we're going to spend the night here," he asked, "what are we going to eat?"

The members exchanged significant glances. Without a word

they hurried outside and made their way in the dim light to the trampled area in the snow. While Judge Parker gathered up the kernels of corn, the rest of the members retrieved the apples from the broken twigs and cut down the pieces of suet. Darkness had fallen as they gathered inside the cottage again, munching frozen apples and watching Cousin Sid heat the suet in a frying pan. Doc Hall took down a wire corn popper from the wall.

"What about the birds?" Judge Parker protested feebly.

"We fed them," Doc Hall said, wincing as he bit into a piece of fried suet. "Now let them feed us."

It was moved and seconded that from now on the Lower Forty would do all its winter feeding in the summertime.

Asleep on the Deep

Judge Parker opened another bottle of champagne with a resounding pop and tossed the cork casually over his shoulder to
join a half-dozen others on the stateroom floor. He refilled the
glasses of the Lower Forty, jammed elbow to elbow in the
smoke-filled cabin, and the members all raised them in unison.
"Bon voyage, Beedie," Judge Parker said. "Here's to a happy
crossing on the *Gripsholm*."

B.D. Banks acknowledged the toast with a diffident smile.
"Sure appreciate you fellows driving all the way down from

Hardscrabble in Mr. MacNab's hearse," he murmured, "just to see me off today."

"Dinna fret, mon," Mr. MacNab consoled him, taking another pickled herring from the hors d'oeuvre tray at his elbow. "Fortunately I had a delivery to make in Woodlawn Cemetery on the way, which helped defr-r-ray expenses."

"Wouldn't seem right to let you leave without saying goodbye," Doc Hall insisted, slipping a couple of Swedish American Line matchboxes into his pocket as a souvenir.

"Least we could do," Colonel Cobb agreed, stashing a china ash tray with three blue crowns. "After all, you belong to the club."

B.D. Banks nodded gratefully. Since he had quit his lucrative brokerage business in the city and retired to Hardscrabble, the members of the Lower Forty had been his closest friends. A lonely widower, he had come to rely on the warm companionship the club offered, and with the help of the members had learned to hunt and fish and enjoy the out-of-doors for the first time in his life. There are more important things than money, B.D. reflected. "I'm going to miss you," he confessed. "It doesn't seem right taking a vacation all by myself."

"Oh, you'll have a wonderful time," Cousin Sid assured him. "Touring Denmark and Sweden, and then winding up in Ireland for the May fly hatch."

"Not to mention a week's cruise in this floating palace," Doc Hall sighed enviously. "Nothing to do but loaf around the swimming pool, or stretch out in a deck chair and watch the ocean go by."

Mr. MacNab's eyes gleamed. "Or sip a cocktail in the ship's hondsome saloon . . ."

"Salon," Doc corrected him.

"What's the difference," Mr. MacNab shrugged, "as long as ye can get a drink?"

"And the food you'll have!" Colonel Cobb enthused, patting his protruding stomach longingly. "They say Swedish cooking is the best in the world. Just think of the free smörgåsbord every night. . . ."

"Fr-r-ree, did ye say?" Mr. MacNab echoed, and the gleam in his eye became a definite glint.

Outside in the corridor gongs were sounding and stewards were calling, "All visitors ashore!" The members glanced at one another and rose to their feet reluctantly.

"Guess we'd better be going," Doc Hall said, taking a small box from his pocket. "Here's a little going-away present, Beedie. It's some trout flies I tied myself for you to use in Ireland."

"Thought this might remind you of Hardscrabble," said Cousin Sid, handing him a gallon of local maple syrup.

Judge Parker produced a balsam pillow, lettered I PINE FOR YOU AND THEN BAL-SOME. "Just a little breath of home," he said softly.

"And here's a bound volume of last year's Hardscrabble *Gazette*," Colonel Cobb said, "to read on the voyage over."

B.D.'s eyes blurred as Uncle Perk presented him with a jug of Old Stump Blower. "Help to wash down the taste o' that furrin licker," he grunted.

They shook hands one by one and left the stateroom. B.D. glanced around, puzzled. "Where's Mr. MacNab?"

"Probably he ducked out because he didn't have a present," Judge Parker suggested, a little harshly. He clapped B.D. Banks affectionately on the shoulder. "Have fun, Beedie," he urged, following the others into the corridor, "and don't forget to drop us a line."

The stateroom was suddenly silent after they'd gone. B.D. strolled up to the top deck, which was crowded with passengers shouting farewell to friends and relatives on the pier below. He started toward the rail to wave to the Lower Forty, but his throat was strangely tight, and he turned away and walked instead to the opposite side of the deck, fighting a mounting feeling of dejection. For a moment he was tempted to leave the ship and rejoin his fellow members on the pier, but the whistle gave a deafening blast, the last gangplank was hoisted, and the liner moved majestically into the current of the North River.

Swallowing the solid lump in his threat, B.D. stood alone at the rail, not even looking at the Jersey shore. The Statue of Liberty receded in the distance; they passed through the Narrows and the Lower Bay, and he gazed blankly at the unbroken horizon of sea and sky. He was feeling more and more despondent as he thought of the good friends he'd left behind. What fun was there in a vacation, after all, when there was no one to share your fun? No, there are some things that money can't buy.

The deck was deserted, and he realized it was almost dinnertime. With a heavy heart he strolled down to his lonely stateroom and opened the door, then halted abruptly at the unmistakable sound of snoring. Stepping back into the corridor, he consulted the number on his key. Yes, he had the right room. He entered again, snapped on the light and gazed incredulously at the slumbering form on the second cot, a half-empty champagne bottle cradled in one arm. Mr. MacNab's eyelids fluttered and he blinked at B.D. "Wher-r-re ar-r-r-e we?" he muttered.

"We're out in the ocean," B.D. gasped.

"Have we dropped the pilot yet?"

B.D. nodded. "An hour ago. You're too late."

"In that case," said Mr. MacNab, promptly sitting erect, "pairhops I can bor-r-row one of your clean shair-r-rts to dress for dinner. I hoppened to note a mite earlier that we both wear-r-r the same size."

B.D. Banks sat down confusedly on his own bed. "But—but what are you going to do?"

"Well, for-r-r one thing," Mr. MacNab replied, "when I get to Ir-r-reland I propose to luik up a former-r-r resident of Har-r-rdscrabble, who owes me a sizable sum for the inter-r-rment of his lamented wife, just befor-r-re he skipped town." The MacNab fingers twitched at the prospect of collecting his just debt. "And with that bit of business oot o' the way, then we can go fishing together-r-r. . . ."

"There's only one difficulty," B.D. Banks interrupted. "They won't let you off the ship without a passport."

"By a verra str-r-range coincidence," Mr. MacNab confided, "I just hoppen to have my passpor-r-rt right her-r-re in my pocket."

B.D.'s face broke into an ecstatic grin. "You sentimental old Scotchman," he accused, "you didn't want me to be alone, did you? You're going to be my guest for the whole trip." He reached happily for the jug of Old Stump Blower. "Now we'll really celebrate...."

Mr. MacNab caught his hand. "Let's finish this champagne instead," he urged, "and save Uncle Pair-r-rk's jug for Ir-r-re-land. I hear-r-r they dinna ken how to make Scotch whisky over ther-r-re."

Mr. MacNab tilted the bottle to his lips, and his eyes moved contentedly over the luxurious appointments of the stateroom. The *Gripsholm* moved evenly in the gentle Atlantic swells, an orchestra sounded in the distance, and he could hear the first gong of the steward announcing dinner. He passed the bottle to B.D. Banks and heaved a nostalgic sigh.

"Aye, it only goes to show you the MacNab clan has come up in the wor-r-rld," he mused. "My puir grandfeyther-r-r had to stow away on a cattle boat."

Mr. MacNab's Record Salmon

Uncle Perk peered over his spectacles as the members of the Lower Forty Shooting, Angling and Inside Straight Club filed into his store. "Reason I called this here meetin'," he announced, when they were all seated along the meat counter, "the club just had an airmail letter from our fellow member B.D. Banks in Ireland." He handed an envelope to Judge Parker. "I figgered the Judge could read it out loud to everybody."

Judge Parker studied the envelope thoughtfully, reversed it and peered at the return address on the back flap. "Gresham

Hotel, Dublin," he mused. "Wonder how Mr. MacNab has been making out, hitchhiking along on Beedie's fishing trip."

"Maybe, if you opened that envelope, you'd find out," Doc Hall suggested impatiently.

The Judge slit the envelope with his forefinger and extracted a long, handwritten letter. "H-m-m-m," he murmured as he scanned the contents. "Well, well, well." He shook his head. "I'll be damned," he frowned. His eyes moved down the page and he chuckled to himself. "Isn't that just like Mac!" Suddenly he sat forward with a gasp of astonishment. "Well, what do you know!"

"We don't know anything," Colonel Cobb scowled, drumming his fingers on the counter, "until you start reading."

"Mr. MacNab got a world-record salmon," the Judge announced incredulously. "Listen to what Beedie says. . . ."

Mr. MacNab's record salmon [B.D. Banks's letter reported] was more or less a coincidence. B.D. and his stowaway companion had dropped in at a village pub one night to refresh themselves after an arduous day's fishing on the Connemara streams, and Mr. MacNab had started his customary argument with the other patrons at the bar. It was his contention that the Scottish methods of poaching were vastly superior to those of the Irish, a statement that never failed to evoke heated replies and usually a couple of rounds of drinks.

"Take my grandfeyther-r-r, God rest his soul," Mr. MacNab challenged them. "Why, he could remove a single hair-r-r fr-r-rom a hor-r-rse's tail, tie it in a noose and slip it ar-r-round a salmon so gently that the fish wouldna ken it was caught till it found itself fr-r-rying in a skillet."

A heavy-set stranger beside him shrugged. "Sure, our technique is far more refined in Ireland," he countered. "We merely slip a hand under the salmon and tickle its belly until it closes its eyes in delight, whereupon it may be lifted onto the bank, still chuckling."

"Another effective procedure," a second patron suggested, "is to chase the salmon round and round a shallow pool until it's too tired to swim any more." He sipped his Guinness reflectively. " 'Tis a rather energetic method," he admitted, "so it might not be familiar to a Scot."

Mr. MacNab bristled. "I'll have ye know that my grandfeyther-r-r was well vairsed in every tr-r-rick of the tr-r-rade," he retorted. "Ar-r-re ye acquainted with the device of bur-r-rning the water-r-r, for example? I'd be glad to describe it, but my glass is a wee bit empty."

The burly stranger beside him signaled the publican for another round.

"Fairst my grandfeyther-r-r would make sure ther-r-re were no bailiffs ar-r-round," Mr. MacNab explained, "and also squar-r-re the local police with a dr-r-rap of Scotch whisky— of the cheapest br-r-rand, of course. This done, the old gentleman would pr-r-roceed to the stream with a thr-r-ree-pr-r-ronged for-r-rk on a long handle, followed by an assistant car-r-rying a sod of peat soaked in paraffin oil. While his helper held the bur-r-rning peat over the pool, my grandfeyther-r-r would wait till a salmon was attr-r-racted to the light, jab the for-r-rk into its back and estimate as he lifted it out of the water pr-r-recisely how much it would fotch at the local hotel."

The stranger next to him shrugged again. "An Irishman

wouldn't be so pecuniary-minded," he observed. "And he'd be using an electric torch." He paused as the publican set the drinks before them. "Personally I find the most productive method is to stretch a net across the river, and have an assistant drag a second net upstream toward the first. Naturally this requires great skill and dexterity, particularly if the stream guards are nearby."

"Aye, there's always a sairtain r-r-risk," Mr. MacNab agreed sadly. "That was why my grandfeyther-r-r had to leave rather hur-r-riedly for the States." He touched glasses with his host. "How do ye hoppen to ken so much about it?" he asked curiously.

The publican leaned across the bar. "Perhaps you're not aware," he informed Mr. MacNab, "that the man you're talking to is none other than Dennis O'Rourke, the most highly respected poacher in these parts."

Dennis acknowledged the tribute with a modest smile.

"Last year Dennis was summoned to appear in court," the publican confided to Mr. MacNab, "and all the local wardens and guards and police, who'd been awaiting this golden opportunity for years, showed up to testify against him. The only one who failed to appear was Dennis. Whilst all the guards were waiting in court, he poached the stream unmolested, and earned enough in one day alone to pay his fine and still show a handsome profit."

Mr. MacNab gazed at his companion with new respect. "That's one tr-r-rick my grandfeyther-r-r never-r-r thought of," he conceded.

" 'Tis an exacting profession, surely," Dennis sighed, "but it offers an ambitious young man an opportunity for advancement. As a chief poacher becomes more venerable, he turns over his duties to his assistant, while he retires to the shore and drinks poteen."

"Poteen?" Mr. MacNab echoed. "What's that?"

"Would ye never be hearing of the fine Irish potable made here in the bogs?" the publican exclaimed. "Though I'm not surprised, at that, for 'tis only for the elite. Poteen is one of the few beverages in the world which never has to be advertised, since it can stand on its own two feet, even though the same can't always be said of its consumers."

"I suppose ye'll be telling me next that it's better-r-r than Scotch whisky," said Mr. MacNab.

Dennis O'Rourke smiled condescendingly. "A friend in the Highlands sent me a bottle of Scotch once," he recalled, "and I could get neither taste nor effect from it, so I rubbed it on my rheumatic knee, acquired as a result of my profession. It made the knee worse."

"I'd like to somple this poteen ye're br-r-ragging about," Mr. MacNab sneered.

"Would ye now?" Dennis said affably. "Then I'll take ye tomorrow to a small lake I know which has some fine salmon in it. The fishing is at its best right now, due to the fact that the owner is visiting in Cork. I'll bring ye some of my own homemade poteen to enjoy while we're trolling."

The following afternoon at dusk Mr. MacNab and his newfound friend set out across the lake in the absent owner's skiff, to which Dennis happened to have a key. The salmon were not striking, so Dennis rested his oars and handed Mr. MacNab a large earthenware jug. "Have a sip of this," he offered, "to make the fish start biting."

Mr. MacNab placed the jug to his lips and took a long gulp. His first impression was that he had swallowed a space rocket. His throat was on fire, his eyes filled with tears and he could feel his scalp crawling. He let out a gasp, and in the dim light his breath had a lurid glow like a flame thrower. He opened his mouth to speak, but only a deep croak emerged.

"Have another sip, do," Dennis urged him. "This whole jug is for you."

Mr. MacNab thought quickly. "Look yonder," he said hoarsely, pointing over his friend's shoulder. "Isn't thot a salmon r-r-rising?"

Dennis turned to examine the lake behind him, and Mr. Mac-Nab tilted the jug over the side and poured its contents into the lake. He placed the empty jug to his lips just as Dennis turned back to him, and went through an elaborate pantomime of swallowing.

"Aye, it's mar-r-rvelous," he murmured. "Almost as guid as Scotch. . . ."

Dennis was staring past him at the water, and Mr. MacNab peered over the side, puzzled. A huge salmon had floated to the surface and was bobbing belly up beside him. He grabbed it by the tail and hoisted it into the boat, and they blinked in amazement at the inert form at their feet.

" 'Tis a trophy fish surely," Dennis whispered in awe. "Whatever could have killed it?"

"Pairhops it drr-rank itself to death," Mr. MacNab suggested.

Dennis seized the oars. "We'll take it back to my house and

weigh it," he said excitedly, rowing toward shore, "and celebrate with another jug of poteen."

Mr. MacNab's face paled at the prospect. "You go ahead,
Dennis," he faltered. "I'll join ye later. . . ."

Judge Parker turned the page of B.D. Banks's letter and
read the final paragraph. "Mr. MacNab's face was still pale when
he showed up at our hotel," B.D. concluded, "and he lay on his
bed with a jug of Uncle Perk's Old Stump Blower, letting it
trickle slowly down his throat. Said it was like soothing syrup.
He hasn't dared go back to weigh his salmon since, but every
time he takes another drink he swears it would have gone a
pound more. By the time we return to Hardscrabble, I predict
it will top the world record."

Cousin Sid's Shipwreck

The rasping of saws and thudding of hammers assailed Cousin Sid's startled ears as he returned to his camp on Pleasant Lake after several days in Boston at the annual High-School Principals' Convention. His front yard was filled with the cars of his fellow members, he noted in bewilderment, and an emergency meeting of the Lower Forty Shooting, Angling and Inside Straight Club seemed to be in progress inside. He skirted a huge pile of fresh plywood, climbed over several rolls of tar paper and calking material stacked beside the entrance and pushed

116

open the door. His jaw sagged. "Wh—what's going on here, fellows?" he gasped.

The interior of the camp was a scene of utter confusion. Sawdust and shavings were knee-deep around the room, a portable power lathe had been screwed onto the top of his television set, and blueprints and technical plans were spread out over every inch of table space. Doc Hall was cutting up a twelve-inch oak plank, using an arm of Cousin Sid's best leather chair for a sawhorse; and Judge Parker, on his hands and knees, was busily nailing a full-scale paper diagram onto the living-room floor.

"Just in time, Sid," he shouted, "to start cooking supper. We've been working so fast all day, we haven't had anything to eat."

Cousin Sid stifled a moan as Colonel Cobb and Mr. MacNab propped a two-by-four on end, while Uncle Perk, balancing atop the bookcase, spiked it securely to the ceiling. "Would somebody tell me," Cousin Sid pleaded, "just what you're building?"

"It's a do-it-yourself boat," the Judge said casually, resuming his hammering. "We decided this was the most convenient place to assemble it, particularly since you forgot and left your camp key hanging on a nail in the woodshed. How about some supper?"

"But the lake's still frozen over," Cousin Sid stammered. "Why do you need a boat in such a hurry?"

"We're taking it down to Florida," Doc Hall explained, absent-mindedly sawing halfway through the leather arm of the chair as he turned his head to speak. "Mr. MacNab has donated the use of his hearse . . ."

"At a slight fee to cover the wear-r-r and tear-r-r," Mr. Mac-Nab interposed quickly.

". . . and we'll strap the boat on top and drive down to the land of sunshine for a little tarpon fishing." Doc picked up another plank and swung it around, upsetting a lamp and knocking a couple of pictures off the wall.

Cousin Sid sat down weakly on a keg of nails. "What kind of boat is it going to be?"

"Well, as a matter of fact, we're not quite sure," Colonel Cobb admitted. "*Field & Stream* sent us several different plans to choose from. There's one for a dory, and another for a bay skiff and another for a john boat. So we thought we'd sort of put them all together and decide what it was when we finished."

Judge Parker rose to his feet and picked up a set of directions. "All right, let's get going," he ordered briskly. "We're wasting time." He scowled through his spectacles at the fine print. "Insert glass pane in front of perch," he read aloud, "and bore a six-inch circular hole for entrance and exit." His face grew puzzled as he continued. "Mount on vertical ten-foot pole . . ."

Doc Hall snatched the directions from him and studied them for a moment. "These are plans for a bird-house," he announced in disgust.

"They don't put the same kind of lenses in spectacles any more," the Judge complained, reaching for another set of directions. "Okay, here we are. Let's see now. Fit cockpit drains P/S about 1½-inch diameter through hull fittings M and fabricate stud guides to suit beveled guards, allowing room for ¾-inch rabbit . . ."

"You haven't by any chance got hold of some plans for a rabbit hutch?" Colonel Cobb inquired uneasily.

Judge Parker ignored him. "Through-bolt all cleats and anchor rode chocks into deck (see figure 27b) and fasten securely with nine-inch screws (flathead) . . ."

"No need to get personal," Doc Hall bristled.

"Long'l side deck header 1¼ by double 2½ No. 12's into frame head," the Judge continued reading, "and optionally bevel to suit inner trim coating for raked sides." He lowered his spectacles and wiped his forehead. "On second thought, it might be easier if we nailed the planks right onto the floor," he suggested. "We can follow the outline on the paper diagram."

"How are you going to move the boat later?" Cousin Sid asked hollowly.

"Oh, we'll just saw out the floor around it," the Judge said, seizing a handful of spikes. "That way we we've got our hull already built."

Uncle Perk studied the front elevation in the blueprint and scratched his head. "This here looks to me like a plain open rowboat," he pointed out. "Hadn't we oughter have some kind of roof over our heads, in case that Floridy sun gets too hot?"

"Let's build a cabin cruiser instead," Colonel Cobb suggested eagerly. "We can enlarge the diagram a little to include Cousin Sid's kitchen stove, so we'll have a galley to cook on."

"How about taking in Cousin Sid's bedroom while we're at it," Doc Hall chimed in," so that we can all sleep on board?"

"Might be the simplest idea to calk the walls and put in a centerboard and rudder," Judge Parker nodded, "and lug the whole camp down to Florida."

"We could put a keel under the outdoor pr-r-rivy," Mr. Mac-Nab beamed, "and tow it along behind."

Uncle Perk shook his head. "Only thing I'm wonderin'," he murmured, "how're we gonna git this here camp on top of the hearse?"

There was a thoughtful silence. "I guess Uncle Perk is right," Judge Parker admitted. "Let's drive down to Florida and rent a boat when we get there."

"That means we can start right away," Doc Hall said happily, dropping his crosscut saw and dusting the shavings from his knees. "All we have to do is grab our rods and we're off."

"Wait a minute, fellows," Cousin Sid protested, as his fellow members hurried past him toward the door. He gazed at the maze of planks and struts and crisscrossed two-by-four studs that filled his living room. "Who's going to take this thing apart?"

"Dinna fret, Sidney," Mr. MacNab consoled him. "We'll ask *Field & Str-r-ream* to send ye a complete buik of directions." He added over his shoulder, "It's entitled *How-to-Undo-It-Your-r-rself*."

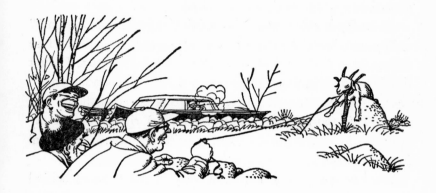

No Hunting or Trespassing

Uncle Perk scowled over his spectacles at the customer who had interrupted the regular meeting of the Lower Forty Shooting, Angling and Inside Straight Club. With a grunt of irritation he knocked out his battered corncob, lowered his hunting boots from the top of the desk and clumped over to the hardware counter. "Wal naow, Potgut," he snarled, "what do *yew* want?"

Potgut Peavey stole an uneasy glance at the group seated around the potbellied stove at the rear of the store and lowered his voice a little. "I'd like a coupla pounds of nails."

121

"Fixin' to do some carpenter work?" Uncle Perk inquired suspiciously, weighing out the nails and dumping them into a paper bag.

"Not exac'ly," Potgut murmured. "I'm puttin' up some signs."

Judge Parker sat erect with a jolt. "What kind of signs?"

"Postin' signs," Potgut admitted. He swung around to face the circle of belligerent faces. "Now look here, fellas, I don't like it no more'n you do, but now all the deer hunters crowd onto my place till I ain't even safe inside my own house any more. This morning they put two bullets right through my kitchen window." He picked up the nails defiantly. "I'm postin' in self-defense."

The members shook their heads as the door closed behind Potgut. "Well, there goes another good grouse cover," Doc Hall sighed. "The whole of Back Road is closed to hunting now."

"Let alone half the farms around Beaver Meadow," Colonel Cobb added.

"You can't rightly blame a farmer for losin' patience," Uncle Perk pointed out in all fairness, "when hunters leave his pasture bars down or use a pair of pliers to cut through his bob-wire fence. And then when he gets home from chasin' his cattle, he finds a pile of empty beer cans on his front stoop and somebody's backed a car acrost the lawn and tipped over his privy."

"Any hunter who'd abuse a farmer's hospitality like that," Judge Parker muttered, "should be forced by law to wear a doeskin jacket and a pair of antlers strapped to his forehead, and crawl through the woods on his hands and knees on the opening day of deer season."

"There's nothing wrong with deer hunting, of course," Colonel Cobb said. "I'll admit I like to stalk a big buck myself, tracking it in the snow and creeping up until I get it in my Lyman. Most deer hunters are sportsmen like everybody else. No, it's a few out-of-state hoodlums and local no-goods who load up on redeye and fire at everything they see, let alone what they don't see. That's what gives the sport a bad name."

"They not only spoil it for themselves," Cousin Sid agreed sadly, "they spoil it for upland-game hunters and fishermen and bird watchers and picnickers and all the rest of us. I wonder what's the answer."

"Maybe the state should have a special license for deer," Colonel Cobb suggested, "and require a registered guide."

"I've got a better answer," Doc Hall said vindictively. "Wait till bird season is all over, and then turn the meat hunters loose in the woods and let 'em shoot it out."

Judge Parker's face was serious. "I'll tell you what's the answer," he said slowly. "Private hunting is the answer. If this irresponsible minority is allowed to invade the countryside every year, drinking and shooting livestock and leaving a wake of death and devastation like Sherman's army, there'll be NO HUNTING OR TRESPASSING signs around every inch of land in the whole East. Another ten years, the way it's going, and free public hunting will be a thing of the past."

"I hope I never live to see the day," Colonel Cobb frowned.

"You won't live to see it," the Judge retorted, "if you stick your neck outdoors while this red-coated rabble is around."

"I'm afraid the Judge is right for once," Doc Hall nodded. "The posting signs in this town alone have doubled in the past couple of years. About the only place we've got left to hunt is the Widow Libbey's lower forty."

"I dunno how much longer we got that," Uncle Perk said ominously. "Mebbe you ain't heard that somebody shot her pet goat yesterday. Drove off and left it lying in the pasture. Now Effie's plannin' to post her land too."

There was a stricken silence. Mr. MacNab took a deep drag on his pipe and exhaled a thoughtful cloud. "D'ye suppose the guid lady would r-r-reconsider," he asked, "if the misc-r-r-reants were pairsuaded to r-r-reimburse her for the loss of her billy?"

"How could we get them to do that?" Colonel Cobb inquired skeptically.

"Oh, it's all a matter of the pr-r-roper appr-r-roach," Mr. MacNab said with a cryptic smile. "As my grandfeyther-r-r used to say, there's guid in ever-r-ryone, if ye ken how to get it out of them." He started toward the door. "Come along and I'll be verra hoppy to demonstr-r-rate my theory. . . ."

The afternoon sun was waning as the members finished propping the Widow Libbey's deceased and stiffened billy goat against a boulder near the road, with a forked stick under its chin to support it in a natural position. They ran a long rope from its foreleg to a nearby clump of bushes, and hid themselves in the shrubbery. They did not have long to wait. A large convertible with an out-of-state license screeched to a stop. There was the cautious sound of a window being rolled down, then a loud *kapow!* shook the air.

Judge Parker yanked the rope and rose to his feet. A deer hunter in red-checkered pants galloped across the clearing toward the fallen animal, and stared at it in chagrin. As the hunter turned to race back to his car, Judge Parker emerged from the bushes and blocked his way.

"I—I guess I made a mistake," the hunter stammered. "I didn't know it was just a goat."

"It isn't just a goat," the Judge corrected. "It happens to be a very special goat. This is the finest imported breeding stock, son of Gesundheit out of Heidi's Pride of the Matterhorn, and it is worth exactly fifty clams." He added, as the visitor opened his lips to protest, "You can pay me now or take the case to court."

"Personally I wouldn't advise that, brother," Doc Hall warned, stepping out of the bushes. "The Judge in this town happens to be a mean-tempered old scoundrel, and he'd be apt to make it a hundred just for spite."

The visitor paid off hastily, and his convertible disappeared in a cloud of dust. As the Judge pocketed the money a second car could be heard in the distance.

"Pr-r-rop up the late lamented," Mr. MacNab shouted. "We've got another-r-r customer-r-r-r."

The members had barely time to get back to the cover of the bushes when a local pickup truck halted beside the clearing and a rifle shot rang out. A gangling youth sprinted toward the goat, unsheathing his hunting knife, and bent over it. He whirled as Judge Parker cleared his throat significantly behind him.

"The usual price for this goat is fifty dollars," the Judge

said, with a glance at the culprit's ancient Remington, "but for you we'll make it twenty-five plus the rifle."

"Wait a minute, mister," the culprit objected. "This here goat's got two holes in it. I only fired once."

"Probably your bullet bounced off the rock," Doc Hall suggested, "and went back through it again."

Another car was approaching over the hill. "Hur-r-r-ry up and pay," Mr. MacNab urged impatiently. "Ye're holding up the whole line. . . ."

The shades of evening had fallen when the Lower Forty decided to call it a day. Judge Parker counted the take for the afternoon and chuckled contentedly. "Two hundred and sixty dollars," he reported to the club, "not to mention three rifles, one slightly used spare tire and a pair of red hunting pants in fair condition. That ought to be enough to keep the Widow Libbey from posting her land"—he winked at Mr. MacNab—"with the compliments of the deer hunters."

"As my grandfeyther-r-r used to say," Mr. MacNab reminded him, "ther-r-re's guid in ever-r-ryone, if ye ken how to get it out."

"By the way," Doc Hall asked, "what are we going to do with Heidi's Pride of the Matterhorn?"

"We'll drop it off at Potgut Peavey's on the way home," Uncle Perk said. "He wouldn't know the difference from venison anyways."

Another October

"Wisht the Jedge would hurry and git here," Uncle Perk grumbled. "Sun's gettin' warm, and them pa'tridge ought to be peckin' around for their breakfast."

"What's the idea, keeping everybody waiting," Doc Hall asked impatiently, "the very first day of grouse season?"

"He had to drive over to Waterbury, Vermont, las' night," Uncle Perk explained, "and get that puppy of his that Earl Twombly's been trainin'."

His fellow members looked at Uncle Perk in pleased surprise.

"Well, I'm glad he's changed his mind," Cousin Sid beamed. "He kept saying he'd never hunt over little Toby."

Colonel Cobb frowned. "That isn't why he's bringing the pup back." He took a folded note from his pocket. "He gave me this advertisement yesterday to put in the paper. 'For sale: two-year-old English setter, male, son of October I. Partly trained, ready for the field. Any reasonable offer accepted.' " The Colonel returned the note to his pocket. "Told me he'd decided to get rid of him. Reminded him too much of what happened to old October."

His fellow members nodded in unhappy recollection. Last fall a speeding car had struck down the old dog as he trotted out of the Judge's yard, and then had kept on going. October managed to haul himself back to the house, his hind legs dragging, and stretched out on the doorstep and gave a final groan. Judge Parker picked him up in his arms, grasped a shovel and walked alone to the top of the hill behind his house. And the following day the Judge sent October's year-old son away to board at Earl Twombly's kennels.

"Said he'd never again have another dog of his own," Colonel Cobb added. "Couldn't bear to go through it twice."

"I know how he feels," Cousin Sid said sympathetically. "If anything ever happened to my little Duke . . ."

"I feel the same way about that pointer of mine," Doc Hall agreed, and sighed. "It's pretty hard on the Judge."

Uncle Perk locked his fingers behind his neck. "It's a mite hard on the puppy, too," he mused.

A station wagon halted before the store, and Judge Parker

hurried in. "Suppose I've got time to drop the young dog off at the house before we start?" he inquired.

"We're late already," Doc Hall objected. "Leave him in the car and let's get going. We're missing the best part of the morning."

Uncle Perk climbed into the front seat of the station wagon and turned to drop his canvas hunting bag behind him. October II was standing on the rear seat, shivering with excitement. He was the image of his father, Uncle Perk observed, with the same dark patch on his face, the same deep-set brown eyes that fastened on Uncle Perk and never wavered, the same lolling tongue that licked his hand as he stowed his gun on the rack behind the seat. Toby's gangling legs hadn't finished feathering out yet, and his deep chest was pointed like a plucked chicken's. "Gonna be as handsome as his old man when he fills out," Uncle Perk murmured.

Judge Parker glanced in the rearview mirror at the young setter peering out of the window as they drove. "Down, Toby," he ordered harshly, and the pup settled himself obediently on a blanket. The Judge's face was impassive. "He ought to bring a good price," he said. "Right at the beginning of the season is a good time to sell."

"Reckon they's a lot o' people would like to have him," Uncle Perk observed mildly.

The other cars had already halted at the edge of the Widow Libbey's pasture, and Judge Parker parked beside them. Cousin Sid's Duke and Doc Hall's pointer were whinnying excitedly and tugging at their leads. Toby heard them and rose expectantly, his tail thumping against the rear-seat cushion. The Judge climbed out of the car without a backward glance. Uncle Perk reached behind him for his hunting bag and gun, and Toby's tongue lapped his hand again. The dog made a soft, whining sound in his throat.

"Wouldn't like to let him trot along with them older dogs, Jedge?" Uncle Perk suggested.

"He'll be all right here," Judge Parker replied. "There's a pan of water, and I'll roll the windows down an inch or so to give him air."

"If you was to put him on a leash," Uncle Perk persisted, "I shouldn't mind holdin' him."

A muscle hopped in the Judge's jaw. "He's staying in the car," he said briefly, and strode across the pasture toward the stand of pines at the far side. Uncle Perk followed in silence.

The grouse were none too plentiful, they discovered, as they moved through the familiar covers. Once Cousin Sid's setter made a fine point beside a stone wall, and later Doc Hall's pointer froze on a woodcock and brought it back to Doc in a perfect retrieve. The Judge watched, and his face tightened. "Reminds me of the way old October used to return a bird," he recalled. "He'd hold it in his mouth so gently he wouldn't crush a feather, and rear up and put his paws on my chest and let me". . . . He broke off abruptly.

The sun was high when they halted for lunch beside a small brook at the other side of the Libbey land. The members stretched out under the pines, while the two dogs made for the water, which they lapped eagerly. The air was still, and from the direction of the parked cars they could make out a steady muffled barking, blended with an occasional high wail. Uncle Perk glanced at the Judge, but he didn't seem to hear.

Colonel Cobb unwrapped a sandwich. "Well, where are we going to try after lunch?" he asked.

"How about the old barn cover," Doc Hall suggested, "where October made that great point last year . . ."

He caught himself, too late, and glanced guiltily at the Judge. It had been October's last point, the afternoon before he was killed; he had pinned three grouse in front of him, holding staunch until the last one had flushed. Judge Parker's face tightened at the pang of recollection, and his voice was a trifle unsteady.

"No sense keeping you fellows from hunting there," he said, trying to sound casual. "I'll stroll along and watch."

Uncle Perk started to take a sandwich from his hunting jacket, and then slid it back into the pocket unnoticed. He gave a sudden snort. "Now, if that don't beat everythin'," he grunted. "I went and left my lunch back in the car." He rose to his feet. "You fellers go ahead and eat, and if I don't git back before you finish, I'll catch up with you at the old barn cover."

The tang of apples was heavy in the air as the other members started through the ancient orchard, the two dogs cutting back and forth ahead of them. Judge Parker's gun was cradled in his arm, and he walked with eyes lowered, remembering that golden day last fall. In his mind he could see old October, straightened out in a classic point, his body rigid, one foreleg cocked. The Judge lifted his eyes. October II was standing under an apple tree just ahead, his body so tense that it shook, his right foreleg drawn up. Cousin Sid's Duke and Doc Hall's pointer were backing him, motionless. Uncle Perk stepped out from behind a clump of bushes.

"Better walk in on him, Judge," he suggested. "Toby's only a pup, he might not hold too long."

Judge Parker took a couple of steps forward, swallowing a lump in his throat. Toby did not budge; he was like a statue of marble, a memorial to another dog that had hunted there before him. Then there was a thunder of wings, the Judge's gun spoke once and the grouse tumbled heavily into a pile of slash.

All three dogs broke, but Toby was first, leaping recklessly into the midst of the jagged branches. He emerged with the bird in his jaws, carried it to Judge Parker and reared up and put his paws on the Judge's chest. The Judge took the bird without a word, his eyes stinging, then suddenly he turned away and walked quickly toward the car.

When the others arrived, he was seated in the front seat with Toby's head in his lap. Toby's head did not even turn; his velvety muzzle was flattened on Judge Parker's knee and he was looking up in adoration at the man who had killed his first grouse over him. "One thing I don't understand," the Judge reflected, as Uncle Perk set his hunting bag on the seat beside him. "How did he ever wriggle out of that little crack in the window?"

"Reckon that was my fault, Jedge," Uncle Perk admitted sheepishly. "He jes' plumb slipped out between my legs and went lookin' for you."

The Judge gave him a quick glance, and his hand worked under Toby's neck and ruffled the soft fur. "By the way," he said to Colonel Cobb, "forget about that ad I gave you. There's not enough money in the world to buy this pup."

Uncle Perk reached inside his canvas bag and produced a jug of Old Stump Blower. He pulled out the cork with his teeth and took a contented swallow. "Yes sir," he nodded, passing the jug to the Judge, "I reckin he's gonna follow right in his old man's pawprints."

Cousin Sid's Green Pastures

Uncle Perk tossed another chunk of cordwood into the pot-bellied stove at the rear of his store and scowled as a January gale rattled the tin stovepipe. "Durn winter," he grunted. "Sometimes I think them little woodcock are smarter'n we are. They spend their summers up in Canadey where it's nice an' cool, an' then they migurate down to New England in the fall when the leaves is at their purtiest, an' then, when the weather turns sour, they pack up an' head south to get away from all the snow an' slush. Yes sir, they're a real smart bird."

"They're smart in other ways, too," Colonel Cobb nodded. "They know enough to zag when they're supposed to zig."

"Aye, they'r-r-re so smar-r-rt," Mr. MacNab agreed, "that they even keep on flying after they'r-r-re dead."

"A timberdoodle isn't hard to hit if you know how," Judge Parker observed loftily. "All you have to do is take him at the top of his spin. . . ."

"If it's as easy as all that," Doc Hall goaded, "how come you do so much space exploration with that corn shucker of yours?"

"I guess the hardest part of it is findin' enough birds to shoot," Uncle Perk remarked with an innocent expression, as he rammed tobacco into his pipe with a calloused thumb. " 'Taint everybody can afford to take a week off, f'rinstance, an' drive all the way up to the Canadian border to meet the big migutory flight as it starts down."

The other members of the Lower Forty shifted in their seats and glared at Cousin Sid, whose face was starting to turn a bright autumn red.

Uncle Perk reached in his pocket for a kitchen match. "Sure envied the rest o' you fellers that trip to Maine last fall," he recalled, "while I had to stay back here all alone an' tend store." He rasped the match across the top of the stove. "I kep' thinkin' of you up there in them northern flight covers, with a guide to see that you got the birds, even if he had to shoot 'em for you himself."

He held the match to the bowl of his pipe and peered over the flame at Cousin Sid, who was squirming uncomfortably and tugging at his collar. Uncle Perk's face was guileless.

" 'Course, on the other hand," he mused, "it's like I allus say." He emitted a luxuriant cloud of tobacco smoke. "They ain't no place like home. . . ."

It was Cousin Sid who had suggested the ill-fated woodcock hunt the previous October. "There's nothing like those Maine alder covers when the flight is on," he had assured his fellow members. "Why, Ellis Briggs told me he's counted as many as forty or fifty birds in a single swamp. He says the only way you can avoid getting your limit is to bend your gun barrel in a curve and shoot left-handed from the hip." His eyes shone with excitement. "If all of you can arrange to take a week off," he urged, "I'll write ahead and make the arrangements, and hire a local guide I've heard about. His name's Emmett Pelvey, and he knows the best flight covers."

All the members except Uncle Perk had signed on promptly for the trip, and even Duke Castle, the nonresident member from Baltimore, wired that he would drive all the way up from the South to join them. "We certainly hate to leave you behind like this," Cousin Sid told Uncle Perk sympathetically, "but we promise to bring you back some birds for your freezer."

The distance to the Maine-New Brunswick border proved to be a little more than Cousin Sid had estimated, and Mr. Mac-Nab's hearse had slow going through a driving rainstorm that beat against his windshield all the way. But the skies were clearing as they arrived that night and located the comfortable motel which Cousin Sid had rented for the party. Emmett Pelvey, the guide, was waiting for them on the front steps, looking a little like Rip Van Winkle, with his battered shotgun and elderly pointer sleeping at his feet. He was a lean and taciturn old down-Easter, with a white stubble beard and a conversational stock that was largely limited to the word "ay-uh."

"We'll start first thing in the morning," Cousin Sid told him. "We can split the party up and work different covers, and after we've all gotten our limit, we can spend the rest of the day shooting ducks."

"Ay-uh," said Emmett Pelvey, and sauntered off to his car without further comment.

The following day proved to be something of a disappointment. The covers were bare of birds, and the dogs quartered back and forth in vain. Yesterday's rain had washed the leaves clean, and there was no sign of fresh spatter to indicate a flight. They located only a couple of stray woodcock, both of which Emmett shot because he happened to be in the lead. The members were a little discouraged as they staggered back to their motel that evening.

"Probably we're just a little early," Cousin Sid insisted, in an effort to cheer the downcast party. "The flight should be in tomorrow at the latest, and then we'll have some real shooting. Too bad Uncle Perk won't be here to enjoy it."

"I dinna miss Uncle Pair-r-rk," Mr. MacNab grumbled, "as much as I miss his jug."

The next day was the same story. They put up a pair of wild grouse, both of which Emmett bagged, but they found only one woodcock, which Emmett also knocked down. By the end of the third day's futile hunting, the temper of the Lower Forty had grown increasingly moody, and they had begun to cast dark looks in Cousin Sid's direction. He sat down on the motel steps with a sigh of defeat. "I can't understand it," he admitted, and turned to Emmett Pelvey. "When do you expect the flight will be here?"

"Wal, the way I figger it," Emmett estimated after a moment's thought, "the flight should be here in about eleven months and three weeks."

Cousin Sid gasped. "You mean it's been and gone?"

"Ay-uh," Emmett said. "That big storm last week moved 'em all out." He shook his head. "Too bad you missed it."

"Why didn't you tell us?" Judge Parker demanded.

"You never asked me," Emmett replied.

The Judge's eyes moved accusingly toward Cousin Sid, and Doc Hall and the others made threatening moves toward him. Cousin Sid rose quickly and backed a couple of steps.

"Wal, I guess if you ain't gonna hunt no more," Emmett Pelvey suggested, "you might as well settle up now for what you owe me, so I can go home and git a little rest." He collected the fees for his services from the silent members, and stuffed the bills into his pocket. "Tomorrow I got to guide another out-o'-state party who are coming up to Maine for the woodcock flight."

He picked up his shotgun, hesitated, then took three bedraggled woodcock from his gamebag. "By the way, you might like to take these back with you," he offered generously. "I got more'n I can ever use."

It was late the following evening when Mr. MacNab's hearse pulled up in front of Uncle Perk's store, and the travel-weary members hobbled inside and lowered themselves stiffly onto the cracker barrels around the stove. Uncle Perk was seated in his swivel chair, his rubber-bottomed hunting boots crossed on his desk as he ran a cleaning rod through his shotgun. He glanced briefly over his spectacles at the three woodcock that Cousin Sid laid on the counter.

"Too bad you fellers wa'n't here last week," Uncle Perk murmured, returning to his gun. "That main flight of woodcock come through Hardscrabble the day after you left."

The other members of the Lower Forty caught their collective breath and emitted it in unison in a low, menacing growl. Cousin Sid avoided their eyes and started to edge toward the front door. Uncle Perk held up his shotgun to the light and peered through a gleaming barrel with critical approval.

"Yes sir, I never had better shootin'," he beamed. "Worked all our favorite covers along Mink Brook, an' got my limit every day." He polished his gunstock with an oiled rag. " 'Course I was all alone, so there wa'n't any competition. . . ."

Cousin Sid's pace increased to a brisk run, and he dashed through the front door and slammed it behind him just as a dead woodcock landed against it with a dull thud.

Uncle Perk leaned back philosophically in his swivel chair. "It's like I allus say," he mused. "They ain't no place like home."

How To Carve a Turkey

It had not been Judge Parker's original intention to stage a Thanksgiving feast for the entire membership of the Lower Forty Shooting, Angling and Inside Straight Club. The invitation had come about when he sauntered into Uncle Perk's store a couple of days before the holiday, proudly displaying a twenty-pound turkey gobbler he had brought back from his hunting trip in Carolina. His fellow members had greeted him with that generous enthusiasm and unselfish spirit of camaraderie for which the club is famous.

"How'd you get it?" Doc Hall grunted. "Bait it right up to the trap?"

"Listen, I stalked this old gobbler for a whole week," the Judge insisted. "Finally located him feeding on a live-oak ridge, and I called him in to me and dispatched him with a load of No. 6 chilled at thirty yards. . . ."

"Naow, that's funny," Uncle Perk observed, inspecting the plucked carcass lying on the counter. "I don't see no shot in it no place."

"I aimed right for the head," Judge Parker explained hastily. "I didn't want to spoil the meat."

"Did ye shoot off all the feather-r-rs at the same time?" Mr. MacNab inquired skeptically.

"Naturally I had it cleaned and dressed before I brought it back north," the Judge protested in a hurt voice. "I certainly can't imagine why you're all so suspicious."

"Oh, it isn't that we don't trust you, Judge," Colonel Cobb said, taking a newspaper out of his pocket. "It just so happens that the Hardscrabble *Gazette* exchanges with a couple of papers down in Carolina." He glanced at the Judge's reddening face and read an item aloud. " 'Judge Lyford Parker, a Yankee visitor from the north, won the shot-sticking event in the annual Longleaf Pine Club Turkey Shoot. First prize was a twenty-pound gobbler from the farm of . . .'"

"All right, all right," the Judge conceded, mopping his forehead. He appealed to the grinning circle. "If you fellows promise not to tell my wife, I tell you what I'll do. I'll invite you all to my house for Thanksgiving to share the turkey with me."

Cousin Sid hesitated. "What will your wife say about a big crowd like that?"

"It's nothing to what she'd say," the Judge groaned, "if she ever found out I lied to her about my trophy."

The Parkers' dinner table was small for such a gathering, but Patience Parker added a few card tables and unended steamer trunks to augment it. Since her dining-room chairs were not sufficient for the occasion, Mr. MacNab had lent her some folding chairs from his mortuary parlor, and the guests perched atop telephone directories and sofa pillows to bring their chins to the level of the tablecloth. There was an appreciative murmur of "Ohs" and "Ahs" from the other wives, as Mrs. Parker carried in the big bird on a silver platter and placed it before the Judge. "Are you perfectly sure, dear," she asked him, "that you wouldn't rather have me carve it out in the kitchen?"

"Of course not, dear," Judge Parker said. "Carving the holiday fowl is the traditional prerogative of the male member of the family." His voice took on its familiar courthouse intonation. "It is on this ceremonious occasion that a man assumes his proper role as the proud husband and father, the *paterfamilias,* the head of the . . ."

"Hurry up, dear," Mrs. Parker interrupted. "The turkey's getting cold."

Frowning, the Judge picked up the carving knife and fork, and inspected the bird over his spectacles. His frown deepened. The crisp brown skin covered it like a duck marsh at high tide, obliterating all familiar landmarks, and he had no idea where to begin slicing. Stalling for time, he lowered his knife and fork again. "Before we start," he said, "let's all bow our heads for a moment in a silent grace."

He waited until everyone was looking down, and then prodded the bird experimentally with his forefinger. You'd think they'd furnish some sort of architectural blueprint with these things, he mused. Something to warn the carver where he might hit a concealed plumbing pipe or steel girder. At least they might give you a dotted line to cut along, like those do-it-yourself outfits. He withdrew his hand as the guests lifted their heads again.

"Maybe I'd better turn this bird around," he murmured. "It might be easier to get at it the other way."

The Judge revolved the platter before him, dragging part of the tablecloth with it and upsetting one of his wife's silver candlesticks into the cranberry sauce. He slid his spectacles down on his nose and inspected the turkey again. As far as he could see, the other side looked just like the first one. There were increasing signs of restlessness around the table, and Mrs. Parker whispered, "Don't take so long dear. Everybody's starved."

Desperately the Judge selected a flat surface, which seemed to be reasonably free of suspicious-looking bumps and ridges, and made a tentative incision with the knife blade. A chorus of protest rose from the entire table.

"Not straight down!"

"Carve it across the grain!"

"Cut off the drumstick first!"

Judge Parker lowered his knife and fork. "Of course, if some other member would prefer to carve," he suggested hopefully.

"Oh no, you go ahead," Doc Hall jeered. "You're the *pater-familias* here."

Gritting his teeth, the Judge stuck his fork into the bird and leaned with all his weight. The turkey did a complete somersault in the platter, scattering gravy in all directions. The Judge removed his elbow from the mashed potatoes, straightened up slowly and wiped some spots of grease from his spectacles.

"Try to get a half nelson around its neck," Colonel Cobb advised, "then hook one leg around the thigh in a near grapevine and turn it on its back. That constitutes a pin."

"You should always start with the second joint," Doc Hall suggested. "That's halfway between the first joint and the third joint."

The Judge's lips had set in a tight line. He braced himself, leveled the knife and prepared to go in over the horns. It was —what did the Spanish call it?—the moment of truth. Humming a snatch from *Carmen,* he pirouetted and plunged the blade deep into the flesh, striking the backbone and skidding the turkey off the platter and down the length of the table. It executed a neat ten-strike on a group of saltcellars, narrowly missed Dexter Smeed as it sailed through the air and landed in a far corner of the dining room with a heavy thud. The moment of truth was over.

Patience Parker let out her breath in a resigned sigh. "Pick it up off the floor," she told her husband quietly, "and I'll carve it out in the kitchen as usual."

"Doc doesn't carve, either," Jennie Hall said. "I don't know how he gets along in the operating room."

" 'Tis the same with my Angus," Mrs. MacNab agreed. "He canna slice the tair-r-rkey thin enough."

"The way we do it at our house," Cousin Sid's wife explained, "I do the carving, and Sidney does the dishes afterward."

Patience Parker gave her husband a cold glance as she started for the kitchen. "Not a bad idea," she nodded grimly.

The members of the Lower Forty and their wives lounged comfortably around Judge Parker's living room after the Thanksgiving feast, full of food and satisfaction. Doc Hall glanced up as the Judge appeared in the doorway, an apron tied around his waist and his sleeves rolled up on soapsuds-covered forearms.

"How about some of you freeloaders giving me a hand with all these dishes?" he growled.

Doc shrugged and daintily removed a particle of turkey from his teeth with the tip of his little finger. "Why Judge, you wouldn't want anybody else to help you," he chided. "That's the traditional prerogative of the male member of the . . ." He held up a warning hand as the Judge advanced on him belligerently. "By the way," he said, "maybe you'd like me to tell your wife how you got that gobbler."

Judge Parker opened his mouth to protest, closed it again, and turned abruptly. There was a sound of banging pots and pans in the kitchen, accompanied by a steady mutter of dark oaths. Doc Hall made himself a highball with the Judge's best Scotch, and lit one of his host's expensive cigars. He beamed at Patience Parker.

"The whole secret of turkey hunting," he began, "is to shoot a bird that's already sliced."

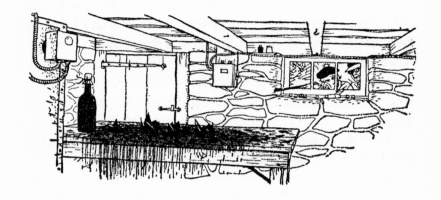

The Elderberry Shoot

It was evident that The MacNab was not himself. He sat alone on a barrel of pickled tripe at the rear of Uncle Perk's store, gazing morosely at a sheet of paper covered with numerals and dollar signs. Now and then he would groan to himself and mutter, " 'Tis a wear-r-ry, wear-r-ry wor-r-rld," the R's echoing in his throat like a death rattle.

Colonel Cobb leaned toward the other members of the Lower Forty. "What's eating Mac?" he whispered. "I never saw him act so depressed."

"His daughter's getting married next month," Judge Parker confided.

Cousin Sid clucked his tongue sympathetically. "I know how he feels," he sighed, "losing his only child. . . ."

"It isn't that," the Judge corrected. "He's just found out that the bride's father has to give the wedding reception, and he's trying to figure out the cost."

Mr. MacNab crumpled the paper in his fist, sprang to his feet and strode toward his fellow members. "I'll be wiped out! Impover-r-rished! R-r-ruined!" he protested. "By the time I've paid for the flower-r-rs and or-r-rchester and all the food. . . ."

"Not to mention the liquid refreshments," Doc Hall reminded him. "Wouldn't be a wedding unless they toasted the bride with champagne."

"Champagne!" Mr. MacNab clapped a hand to his forehead. "I'll have to mor-r-r-tgage my hair-r-rse!" He paused, a faint gleam of hope in his eyes. "Pairhops I could substitute something a wee bit less expensive," he mused, "like some of my wife's homemade elderber-r-ry wine."

Uncle Perk snorted. "Might's well give 'em sody pop. That stuff o' Maggie's ain't got no more kick'n a dead chipmunk."

"Of course, you could spike it up a little," Judge Parker suggested helpfully. "Remember how we used to make home-brew back in prohibition days? Add some yeast and raisins and brown sugar and chopped beef, and a few diced sugar beets for color, and let it ferment."

The gleam in Mr. MacNab's eyes brightened. "How long would the fair-r-r-mentation take?"

"Oh, it ought to work fast," the Judge replied, "if you put the bottles in a warm place. The guests won't be able to tell it from champagne punch."

"Thank ye, Judge," Mr. MacNab said gratefully, smiling for the first time. "Ye've saved me fr-r-rom sair-r-rtain bankr-r-ruptcy."

A few days before the wedding the Lower Forty gathered in the MacNab home for an evening of poker, an occasion made possible by the fact that Maggie MacNab had gone to the city to help her daughter with some last-minute shopping for her trousseau.

"The wine is wor-r-rking fine," Mr. MacNab reported to Judge Parker as the members seated themselves around the bare dining-room table. "There's a dozen bottles down in the cellar-r-r right beside the oil bur-r-r-ner," he began, shuffling a deck of cards, "and the way they're bubbling, they should be r-r-ready in plenty of . . ."

The cards flew from his hands as a muffled explosion shook the house, swaying the chandelier and rattling the chinaware on the shelves.

"The bur-r-rner's blown up!" Mr. MacNab yelled, racing toward the kitchen. "Call the fir-r-re depar-r-rtment, quick!"

He yanked open the door to the cellar, snapped on the light switch and peered below. There was no smell of smoke, no sight of billowing flames. His puzzled gaze moved to the cellar door, studded with bits of broken glass. A fresh red stain was trickling slowly down the panel. "Blood!" he gasped.

Uncle Perk ran a forefinger over the wet stain and sniffed

it thoughtfully. "Smells more to me like elderberries," he observed.

Mr. MacNab caught his breath with a gasp and started down the cellar stairs. Judge Parker grabbed his arm, hauled him back into the kitchen and slammed the door. "You can't go down there," he warned. "The rest of those bottles are apt to explode any minute."

"Oh, my pr-r-recious wine," Mr. MacNab said hysterically, struggling toward the door. "I've got to r-r-remove it fr-r-rom the heat. . . ."

A pair of heavy detonations rocked the air, the cellar door seemed to buckle inward with the concussion, and there was a sharp rattle of glass fragments against the other side of the panel. Mr. MacNab sank onto a kitchen stool, staring at the door blankly.

"How did you cork those bottles?" the Judge asked him.

"I used metal caps," Mr. MacNab said, "and clamped them on secur-r-rely." Another bottle blew up with a roar like a grenade, and he buried his face in his hands. "Whot am I going to do?"

"You can't do anything," the Judge said sternly. "That cellar is like a mine field. Just wait till they've all exploded, and we'll drop around tomorrow and help you mop up."

When the Lower Forty returned, the following morning, Mr. MacNab was pacing up and down the front lawn, his eyes red with lack of sleep.

"Is the bombardment over?" Judge Parker asked.

Mr. MacNab shook his head. "Three more bottles bur-r-rst

after you left," he reported, "and since then there hasna been a sound downstair-r-rs." He led the way to a small cellar window. "Ther-r-re's still five mor-r-re."

The members gazed through the broken pane at a scene of wartime devastation. Shattered glass covered the cellar, several jagged shards were embedded in the timbers overhead, and the cement floor was awash with red wine. On a table beside the furnace were the remaining five bottles, as ominous as ticking bombs.

"I've been waiting all night for them to go," Mr. MacNab sighed. "How long befor-r-re I can go down cellar?"

"Wal, some bottles work slower'n others," Uncle Perk told him. "Might be a week or two before they all blow."

"A week or two?" Mr. MacNab echoed hollowly. "But Maggie's getting home tonicht, and the wedding is Fr-r-riday and all the pr-r-rsents are in the laundr-r-ry room behind the fur-r-rnace"—his voice rose out of control—"not to mention my dr-r-ress shirt that Maggie washed specially for the occasion."

"Maybe we could reach through the window and smash the bottles with a long pole," Cousin Sid pondered.

"I've got a better idea," said Judge Parker. He hurried to his car and returned with a .30–06 rifle. "The only safe way is to shoot 'em, one by one." Mr. MacNab emitted a moan of anguish. "Don't worry, Mac," the Judge added. "This is soft-nose ammo."

"Let's take turns," Doc Hall suggested, "so each member gets a shot. That makes it more sporting."

Mr. MacNab flinched as the Judge aimed through the window. There was a sharp crack and an answering explosion, followed by the patter of falling glass and a low whimper from Mr. MacNab.

"I'm taking the second from the left," Doc Hall announced, putting the rifle to his shoulder. Another bottle exploded, and Mr. MacNab sobbed audibly. "Three to go," Doc said, handing over the rifle with a satisfied smile. "Your turn, Sid."

Cousin Sid scored a bull's-eye and passed the rifle to Colonel Cobb. Mr. MacNab gritted his teeth as the Colonel took careful aim, and the target disintegrated in a shower of glass and wine. "Who's next?" Colonel Cobb asked.

"I canna stond it!" Mr. MacNab screamed in anguish. "Give me that r-r-rifle."

Judge Parker handed him a cartridge and he slid it into the chamber, sighted along the barrel and squeezed the trigger. The bullet shattered the last bottle, continued through the boiler of the furnace and out the other side, drilled a neat hole in the center of Mr. MacNab's shirt hanging on the line, ricocheted off the far wall of the laundry, drove through a wooden partition and buried itself in the radiator of the hearse parked in the adjoining garage. Mr. MacNab lowered the rifle and gazed at the results mutely.

"I'm sorry," Judge Parker apologized in the ensuing silence. "I must have given you an armor-piercing load by mistake."

"Wal, I reckon Mac gits the prize," Uncle Perk said, producing a jug of Old Stump Blower. "At least, this here stuff won't blow up till it's inside you."

Mr. MacNab accepted the prize without a word and started toward the rear of the house.

"Hey, Mac, aren't you going to share that jug?" Doc Hall called after him.

Mr. MacNab paused to gather a mop and pail from the back porch. "I'm saving it for the wedding r-r-reception," he replied over his shoulder as he headed for the cellar. "If I pour-r-r it in a bowl and add some spar-r-rkling water, the guests willna be able to tell it from champagne punch."

To My Gr...
    This le... December 2, 1977
your sixteenth b...

Letter to a Grandson

Word spreads fast in Hardscrabble, and the members of the Lower Forty were waiting with broad grins as Judge Parker strode into Uncle Perk's store, his pockets bulging with cigars and his face wreathed in a beatific smile. Uncle Perk opened the lower left-hand drawer of his desk, took out a jug of Old Stump Blower and set it on the desk blotter. "Congratulations, Jedge," he said. "I calc'late this calls for a celebration."

The Judge's face fell. "How did you fellows find out already?"

"You don't think our local phone operator could resist listening in on a long-distance call, do you?" Cousin Sid said. "Especially when it's from your son in Japan. She told my wife the news, and my wife told Doc's wife and she told Maggie MacNab. Only thing we all want to know—is it a granddaughter or a grandson?"

Judge Parker reached for the jug. "It's a boy," he announced proudly. "Born three hours ago Pacific time. Of course, they're a day ahead of us over there."

"Then what are we celebrating for?" Doc Hall asked. "His birthday isn't till tomorrow."

"Too bad he couldna been bor-r-rn in this countr-r-ry," Mr. MacNab sighed, "so ye'd save those over-r-r-seas toll char-r-rges."

"I'm running a story in this afternoon's *Gazette*," Colonel Cobb said, taking out a pencil. "How much did he weigh?"

"Well, my son was calling from Yokota Air Force Base where he's stationed, and there was a pretty poor connection," the Judge said, "but it sounded like sixteen pounds."

"Must have weighed him on those scales you always use for your trout," Doc commented.

"He said the youngster is the spitting image of me," Judge Parker beamed, as he handed out cigars to his fellow members. "He's named after me, too," he added, his voice growing a little unsteady.

"Better have another swig, Jedge," Uncle Perk urged quickly, shoving the jug toward him. "It's quite a strain becomin' a grandfather all of a sudden."

Judge Parker's Adam's apple moved up and down several times, and he lowered the jug thoughtfully. "My first grandson," he said in an awed tone. "That means another hunter and fisherman in the family." His eyes were shining. "I'll tell him all the things I know. I'll take him on camping trips and teach him to handle a rod and a gun, and when he's sixteen I'll buy him a license and we'll go to Beaver Meadow together and he'll shoot his first grouse over Toby's point. . . ."

Cousin Sid cleared his throat. "Sixteen years from now Toby probably won't be around," he reminded the Judge softly.

"Can't be too sure any of us will be," Uncle Perk shrugged.

There was a little pause. "I guess you're right," the Judge said brusquely. "I guess if I've got something to tell him, I'd better put it down right now."

He lowered himself into Uncle Perk's swivel chair, rolled a sheet of plain paper into the antiquated typewriter and bent over the keyboard, his lips working as he tried to phrase his thoughts. The other members of the Lower Forty stood behind him, watching in silence as his forefinger began to peck at the keys:

To My Grandson:

This letter will be yours on December 2, 1977, your sixteenth birthday. If I am alive then, I will read it to you. If I have checked out before that date, please go off by yourself, alone, and read it aloud.

Three hours ago your father phoned me that you were in this world, that you and your mother were doing well, and that you will bear my name.

So for three hours I have been celebrating your birth

in an orderly and thorough manner. I have given your grandmother a couple of tranquilizer pills to calm her hysterics at the good news. I have notified all your father's friends in town as he requested, so they can celebrate also. I have stopped at the bank and arranged a modest trust fund, which should see you through college. I have had several drinks, and now I am writing a letter for you to open sixteen years later.

I will waste neither your time nor mine in giving you advice. If, by the time you are sixteen, you do not know the meaning and practice of truth and loyalty and courage and honesty, and the deep satisfaction of doing hard work, both physical and mental, then your great-grandfather did a hell of a poor job raising me, and I did a hell of a poor job raising your father.

I am leaving you a few things.

First I leave you your great-grandfather's weapons. He taught me how to shoot a pistol with his .38 Colt Army. I have not fired it since the day he died. I will give it a real good cleaning and put the neat's-foot oil to the holster, and leave it with the same loads that he put in the cylinder himself the last time he dropped the hammer. Also you will receive his .30–30 carbine and his 12-gauge Greener. No buck ever went very far that caught one of my dad's .30–30's behind the foreshoulder. No goose kept flying very long that he centered with a load of 4's.

Next I leave you my old Browning 5-shot 12-bore. I have used that gun so much that it has been reblued and rebuilt twice. Also my scope-sighted Model 70 Winchester

.30–06. Also my house gun, a .357 Magnum Smith & Wesson snubnose. A man who is not ready and able to defend his home does not belong in our family.

Also I leave you my 8½-foot 4-ounce Leonard rod, which is as good as the day it was built, and they do not build them any more. I leave you my 9-foot, 6½-ounce Orvis light salmon rod, which has killed some good fish in Canada and Alaska and Ireland. You may fish some of the same pools with it. I leave you my favorite 8-foot, 3½-ounce dry-fly rod which Walt Powell made for me, and which can lay a No. 12 Spent-wing Coachman on the water slicker than a schoolmarm's leg. All these rods and guns will be cleaned and cased and tagged with your name.

More important, I am leaving you some memories. I hope that through the years they will be your memories, as they have been mine, as they are now your father's, as they were your great-grandfather's once. . . .

The Judge stopped typing abruptly, removed his glasses with a scowl and wiped off some moisture, and put them back on again. His finger moved over the keys more slowly.

I leave you the cold gray dawn and the marshes and the wind and the slap of wavelets and the whistle of wings and the recoil of your gun against your shoulder.

The creak of pack straps in the dark and the thud of moccasins on the steep trail and the deep breathing as you and your hunting partner pack out your deer.

The easy grating of your canoe over a gravel bar and

the snaking out of your line in the last long dusk and the sudden staccato scream of your reel.

The flutter and thump of a turkey gobbler coming down from his roost in that first light when you can count the eyelets of your boots.

The taste of a cold mountain spring as you lie on your belly with your mouth spitting cotton.

The smells that men like to remember—pipe smoke and boot dubbing and Hoppe's No. 9, and fly dope on a red bandanna handkerchief, and wet dog fur steaming by the fire, and the smell of leather that is more like a taste, and the before-breakfast smell of coffee boiling and bacon frying, and the smell of a cottonmouth—the smell of fear —and the fall smells of sweet fern and rotting apples and burnt powder in the frosty air.

I leave you a windy spring night and the shrill of peepers like sleigh bells and the far-off baying of geese heading north in the empty sky.

Swimming stripped in a clear lake under an August moon, and then standing on the shore with a cigarette while the night wind dries your body and the loons call.

An afternoon in October and a bird-dog puppy stanch on his first point, with one foreleg drawn up and his brown eyes fixed and his whole skinny body shivering with the strange new excitement of grouse.

A winter evening with the sleet against the window and a log blazing and a highball and some friends you have hunted and fished with to share your memories with you.

All these and more I leave to you, my beloved grandson. Perhaps I will live long enough to be at your side when they become your memories, too. But if I do not, I raise my glass to you across the years.

Judge Parker pulled the page from the typewriter, leaned back in the swivel chair and took off his spectacles and wiped them again. The other members of the Lower Forty turned away with heads lowered, not speaking.

Uncle Perk reached for the jug. "I figger we'll all drink to that, Jedge," he said quietly.